Science in Saffron

Science in Saffron
Skeptical Essays on History of Science

Meera Nanda

Three Essays
COLLECTIVE

First Edition January 2016
Copyright©Three Essays Collective

ISBN 978-93-83968-08-4

B-957 Palam Vihar, GURGAON (Haryana) 122 017 India
Phone: 91-124 2369023, +91 98681 26587, +91 98683 44843
info@threeessays.com Website: www.threeessays.com
Printed and bound by Chaman Offset Printers, New Delhi

In memoriam

Praful Bidwai   1949-2015
Ajita Kamal   1978-2011

dear friends and comrades

Contents

Introduction

Some years ago, I happened to watch an advertisement for *Rajnigandha paan masala* on TV that stuck a nerve with me. This is how it went:

A bespectacled young Indian man in a tweed jacket is sitting in a classroom in an American campus where a professor is writing some rather complicated looking mathematical equations on the chalk board. The young man appears bored; he is looking out of the window and doodling on his notepad. Speaking in an exaggerated American drawl, the professor asks how much time the class will need to solve a problem, and all the European and Chinese-looking students balk at the task, saying the problem is too tough. Muttering racist-sounding epithets about "you Indians" and "trees," the professor calls upon the *desi*. The Indian student gets up, takes out a small can of *paan-masala* from his jacket and puts some in his mouth. He then walks up to the board and solves the mathematical problem without a moment's hesitation. The American classroom breaks into cheers, and the young man takes a bow. The image of a packet of *Rajnigandha paan masala* appears on the screen with the following voice-over: "जवाब तो हम पहले से जानते थे, सवाल का इन्तिज़ार करना हमारी तहज़ीब है" ("We already knew the answer. Waiting for the question is our culture"). The advertisement ends with a jingle: "मुंह में रजनीगंधा, पैरों पे दुनिया" ("With Rajnigandha in your mouth, the world is at your feet.")[1]

---

1   The advertisement can be viewed at https://www.youtube.com/watch?v=kBbBISCtkv8

With some foresight, the ad-agency could have amassed a considerable fortune by selling this slogan (sans the jingle) to the Sangh Parivar. The young *paan-masala* consuming fellow could have achieved lasting fame as the mascot of the new geeky Indian that we are so love to celebrate.

"जवाब तो हम पहले से जानते थे, सवाल का इन्तज़ार करना हमारी तहज़ीब है" would make an excellent backdrop for any number of "science in the Vedas" events that the Parivar and its allies like to host. The beauty of the slogan is that it can capture the spirit of whatever scientific जवाब you may be in the mood to fit into "the Vedas" on any particular day – robotics, nuclear energy, quantum physics, Einstein, theory of evolution, genetics, consciousness ... the list is limited only by your imagination. Why just the Sangh Parivar, even the Indian Science Congress could have trotted out the slogan for the more colorful sessions during its annual meet in Mumbai in January 2015!

* * *

This book is provoked by the constant assault that on our collective intelligence from those who are convinced that "जवाब तो हम पहले से जानते थे." But it is more than mere irritation that has motivated me. I believe that the constant appropriation of modern scientific concepts and theories for the glory of "the Vedas" is one, if not *the*, central plank on which the myth of Hindu supremacy rests. It is thanks to this myth of "scientific Hinduism" that our preeminent national figures, past and present, habitually sneer at the "superstitions" of Abrahamic religions. It is thanks to this myth that we think of ourselves as a "race" endowed with a special faculty for science. It is thanks to this myth that we go around the world thumping our chests as "scientific Indians" without whom the world science and economy would grind to a halt.

Such myths of national exceptionalism and supremacy are dangerous. Nothing but evil follows when such myths manage to take hold of a nation's imagination.

It is for this reason, this smug, self-adoring myth of the "Vedas" as having all the answers – even before scientific questions were even possible to ask! – must be taken seriously. Each one of its claims must be examined with utmost attention, using the best available evidence that history of science has to offer. After we are done laughing at some of the utterly outlandish claims, we must get down to the serious business of analyzing what they are saying in the light of what we know of how science developed in the modern world and how it differs from other forms of knowing the world. Time has come for intellectuals to step out of their ivory towers to challenge the distortion of history of science for ideological ends.[2]

Such a response has not been forthcoming, or at least, has not been proportional to the enormity of the challenge. The scientific community in India – whose turf is being encroached upon – has offered only a deafening silence so far (with rare exceptions who can be counted on the fingers of one hand). What is even more disheartening is the silence of Indian historians of science against the blatant encroachment of *their* turf.[3] Indeed, the silence of academic historians of science is more worrisome, as it is symptomatic of postmodernist malaise that continues to afflict the humanities and social sciences in India. How can those who cannot utter the words *modern science* without putting them under contemptuous scare-quotes that question the very distinctiveness and legitimacy of the enterprise of science, be expected to start demarcating modern science from Vedic or any other "alternative" knowledge system? How can those who cannot bear to refer to the mainstream, global history of science without qualifying it as "colonial" and "Eurocentric" be expected to turn to the same history for evidence to counter the priority-claims of our nationalist mythmakers?[4]

---

2   Romila Thapar (2015) distinguishes public intellectuals from technical experts and ordinary academic scholars by two necessary qualities: Public intellectuals question authority; and they "defend the primacy of reasoned, logical arguments in explaining the world around us as well as its past." p. 2

3   This refers *strictly* to those historians who specialize in science. History of science is a relatively specialized sub-set of political and cultural history. Mainstream historians, archeologists and other concerned intellectuals, to their credit, have continued to raise their voices against mixing up of myth and science.

4   See for instance Sundar Sarukkai (2014) for a defense of "alternative rationalities" and the importance of "cultural ownership" of science by Indians. Sarukkai's insistence that modern conceptions of physics – mass, energy, motion etc. – must be mapped on to philosophical terms derived from Indian philosophy is no different from the recent intervention by Rajiv Malhotra (2015) to "fit modern science into

This book is meant to take on the substantive claims of those who would saffronize modern science. It offers a detailed and through examination of the priority-claims on behalf of ancient Indian mathematicians and physicians regarding landmark scientific discoveries (the Pythagorean Theorem, zero, genetics and surgery). Such claims have been a fixture of Indian public discourse for a long time, and have been given a fresh impetus at a variety of high-visibility gatherings over the last year of so.

The goal of the book is to save the ancient Indian geometers, mathematicians, physicians and the unknown artisans-craftsmen/women from both the glorification at the hands of the Hindu Right *and* the condescension at the hands of rationalist fundamentalists who see no value whatsoever in anything that predates the Scientific Revolution. This can be done, I believe, by placing their achievements in their own times, and alongside the achievements of their peers in sister civilizations. A comparative history, devoid of presentist biases, can bring the true accomplishments of our ancestors into a sharper focus – something that this book tries to do.

* * *

Claims to the effect that "it is all in the Vedas" –where "all" includes all known facts and artifacts of modern science and technology (yes, the airplanes, too) are not new. Swami Dayananda Sarasvati, the founder of Arya Samaj, had already proclaimed that as far back as around the mid-19th century.[5] Likewise, claims of there being "perfect harmony" between the teachings of Hindu *shastras* and modern science can be

---

Vedic framework." Malhotra is a much admired figure in the Hindu Right circles and has received glowing accolades from Narendra Modi himself. Skepticism toward the universal metanarrative of science has been declared (Prakash, 1994, p.1483) a necessary precondition for recovering the voices of the subaltern. I have defended the universality and objectivity of modern science form its de-constructors in Nanda (2004).

5   The basic idea that motivated Swami Dayananda was this: Because the Vedas are divinely-inspired "books of true knowledge," they *must* contain the basic principles of all sciences, and accordingly, every scientific discovery and technological development of modern times *must* find an expression in them. This amounts to scientization of the Vedas by fiat. See Arvind Sharma (1989).

traced back to the New Dispensation of Keshub Chandra Sen in the late 1800s, and to his more famous protégé, Swami Vivekananda. In his famous address to the World Parliament of Religions in Chicago in 1893, Vivekananda proudly proclaimed the latest discoveries of modern science to be mere "echoes" of Vedanta philosophy.[6]

Thus, the current craze for finding modern science in ancient religious texts is part and parcel of the history of modernity in India. It has been the dominant trope for accommodating modern science with the Hindu belief-system. In the hundred plus years that separate Swami Dayananda and Swami Vivekananda from us in the 21st century, this style of accommodating science and Hindu beliefs has become a part of the common sense of most Indians. It is not considered particularly right-wing or left-wing, as elements of it can be found among people and parties of all political persuasions.

While it cuts across political affiliations, the eagerness for scientific legitimation of Hindu *dharma* is more actively and self-consciously fostered by Hindu nationalists and their allies. Attribution of great scientific discoveries to ancient Hindu *rishi-munis* has been an integral part of the indoctrination of *swayamsevaks* since the very beginnings of the organized Hindu Right in the early decades of the 20th century.

This explains why every time the Hindu nationalists come to power, the first thing they do is to start revising history, with a special place reserved for the history of science.

During their first stint from 1998 to 2004, the BJP-led NDA pushed for introducing degree-courses in astrology, *karma-kanda* (rituals) and "consciousness studies" of Advaitic variety in colleges and universities.[7]

---

6   We explore Swami Vivekananda's views on science and yoga in the last chapter of this book.

7   The prestigious Birla Institute of Technology and Science, in collaboration with Bhaktivedanta Institute now offers M.Phil. and Ph.D. degrees in "consciousness studies." This program sells itself as an "equivalent of a graduate program in 'cognitive studies' in any Western university." But it is hard to imagine any respectable cognitive studies school in the West accepting the fundamental premise that this program operates with: that consciousness is a pre-existing constituent of matter. This is simply Advaita by another name. Bhaktivedanta Institute is the "research" wing of the International Society for Krishna Consciousness, aka "Hare Krishnas." See http://www.bvinst.edu/gradstudies.

Thanks to the policies put in place by NDA 1.0, any aspiring astrologer or priest can get a diploma from public or private institutions that have been given the status of universities.[8]

Now that the BJP-led alliance is back in power, revising history of science is once again on the top of the list of educational "reforms." NDA 2.0 has lost no time in extending its campaign rhetoric of "India First" to history of science. Claims of India's priority in everything from mathematics, medicine and surgery – to say nothing of nuclear weapons, spaceships and other Star Trek-style technologies – have been made by prominent people at prestigious, national-level gatherings. The ball was set rolling by none other than the Prime Minister in his inaugural address at Sir H.N. Reliance Foundation Hospital in Mumbai in October 2014. This was followed by events at the 102nd annual Indian Science Congress in Mumbai in early January, 2015. Other relatively high-visibility events where a seamless continuity between modern science and ancient sciences and myths was on the agenda include the exhibition in Lalit Kala Academy in New Delhi titled "Cultural Continuity from Rigveda to Robotics," and a seminar on Vedic chronology organized by the Sanskrit department in Delhi University, both in September, 2015. Behind all these high-profile events, there are any numbers of "*Shiksha Bachao*" ("save our Education") activists who want this "history" to become a part of school curricula.

Roughly four kinds of appropriations of modern science for the glory of Hindu sages-scientists can be discerned:

1. Staking priority-claims for ancient India for landmark discoveries in mathematics and medicine. The perennial favorites in this category are the Pythagorean theorem, algebra and zero in mathematics. (We will ask "who discovered the Pythagorean

---

Certificate programs offered by training centers associated with Aurobindo Ashram are recognized by IGNOU, Indira Gandhi National Open University.

8   I have tried to document how educational institutionns set up by prominent religious gurus and sects include a variety of pseudosciences as a legitimate part of their curricula. Many of these institutions have been "deemed" as universities. As "deemed universities" they have been given the authority to set their own curricula and hand out degrees and diplomas. Many receive state support in the form of land-grants and tax-breaks. See, Nanda, 2009.

Theorem?" in Chapter 1, while the next chapter will look at the hallowed Indian invention of zero as a number).

2. Erasure of lines of demarcation between myth and histori-
    cal evidence. This was the Prime Minister's chosen rhetorical
    device at the inaugural address at the Mumbai hospital men-
    tioned above. He invoked the elephant-headed god Ganesh as
    evidence for plastic surgery, and Karna, a character from the
    Mahabharata as evidence for "genetic science." (We will exam-
    ine the history of medicine in chapter 3).

3. Erasure of lines of demarcation between science and certified
    pseudosciences like astrology. While this strategy of giving
    sheen of respectability to discarded knowledge has not disap-
    peared from the public sphere, it has not been openly espoused
    from high places lately.

4. A higher kind of pseudoscience that is generated by grafting
    spiritual concepts like *prana* (or breath), *prakriti* or *akasha* (the
    "subtle" material substrate of nature) on to physicists' concepts
    of "energy" and "ether"; karmically determined birth and re-
    birth on theories of evolution of species; *chakras* with actual
    neural structures, so on and so forth. (Swami Vivekananda
    was the pioneer of this kind of scientization and we will exam-
    ine how he re-wrote Patanjali's *Yoga Sutras* in a scientistic vein
    in the final chapter of this book).

* * *

Why such mental gymnastics? Why this national itch to be crowned "First"?[9]

What look like obvious, and even laughable, contortions begin to make perfect sense when we understand what our saffronizers are re-

---

9   Very similar in spirit to the great eagerness of Indians to have their names
    recorded, for most bizarre feats, in the Guinness Book of Records. According to
    Vinay Lal, nearly one-tenth of the mail that the Guinness headquarters in London
    receives is from Indians. Where else but in India will you find a " World Record
    Holder Club" whose president has "changed his name from Harparkash Rishi to
    Guinness Rishi"? see https://www.sscnet.ucla.edu/southasia/History/Independ-
    ent/guiness.html

ally up to. What is it that they seek to accomplish by their constant and desperate attempts to claim the stamp of "science" for the worldview they want to propagate?

We have to understand that the Hindu nationalists are not in the business of history-writing, even though they may use historical evidence if and when it suits them. No, what they are doing is fabricating a heritage that we are supposed to kneel before in awe and wonder and feel special about. While no history is completely free of biases and errors, historians at least try to correct their narratives in the light of better evidence. Heritage-makers, on the other hand, thrive on errors and biases. The torturous logic, the flights of fancy, the mental gyrations are no circus: They are the tools of the trade needed to create the myth of the "scientific Indian," the bearer of the ancient Hindu heritage which was scientific – in the sense of *Science as We Know it Today, or SaWKiT)* – even before SaWKiT was even born.

The distinction between history and heritage brought out by David Lowenthal in his well-known book, *The Heritage Crusade and the Spoils of History*, is relevant to the Indian situation:

> Heritage is not "bad" history. In fact, heritage is not history at all; while it borrows from and enlivens historical study, heritage is not an inquiry into the past, *but a celebration of it*; not an effort to know what actually happened, *but a profession of faith in the past tailored to present day purposes....* [10]

Again

> Heritage is not a testable or even a reasonably plausible account of some past, but *a declaration of faith in that past....* Heritage is not history, even when it mimics history. It uses historical traces and tells historical tales, but these tales and traces are stitched into fables that are open neither to critical analysis nor to comparative scrutiny..... [11]

And again:

> Heritage is immune to critical reappraisal because it is not erudition but catechism; what counts is not checkable fact but credulous allegiance. Commitment and bonding demand uncritical endorsement and preclude dissenting voices. .... *Prejudiced pride in the past is not a sorry consequence of heritage; it is its essential purpose.* [12]

---

10 Lowenthal, 1998, p. X. emphasis added.
11 Lowenthal, 1998, p. 121. Emphasis added.
12 Lowenthal, 1998, p. 121-122, Emphasis added.

The "scientific Vedas" rightfully belong to the "Incredible India!" campaign which sells Indian heritage primarily to foreign tourists, with the difference that the "heritage sites" for the former are not physical but textual, and the target audience includes Indians first and foreigners only secondarily. The way the "scientific heritage" is constructed and sold, however, is turning Indians into tourists to their own history. The very idea of such a narrative being taught to school children as history of science is frightening indeed.

It is clear that this enterprise is aimed not at educating but, to use Lowenthal's apt words, at creating a "prejudiced pride" in India's past through "celebration" and "declaration of faith" in it. Indeed, this is exactly what the heritage-fabricators openly profess.

A case in point: When the Prime Minister Modi invoked Ganesh from mythology, and Karna from the *Mahabharata* as "evidence" that plastic surgery and genetic science existed in ancient India, he explained his motive for this foray into mythology in the following words:[13]

> We have our own skills. Now, we are not new to medial science…. We can take pride in the world of medicine. Our nation was great one time. … What I mean to say is that ours is a country that once had these abilities [for advanced medicine]. We can regain these abilities.

The PM is hardly alone. Indian Firsters routinely claim that by highlighting the scientific accomplishments of ancient Hindus, they are actually trying to promote a culture of science and scientific temper. This is how the argument unfolds: Indians are heirs to a great civilization which promoted reasoned inquiry, which then led to scientific ideas which are only now being "rediscovered" by modern science. As the beneficiaries of this great civilization, we ought to be inspired by it, reclaim its scientific spirit and produce world-class science again. While they would not put it so starkly, even some secular historians of

---

13 "हमारा अपना ये कौशल्य है, अब मेडिकल साइंस में हम नए नहीं हैं। … मेडिकल साइंस की दुनिया में हम गर्व कर सकते हैं, हमारा देश किसी समय क्या था… कहने का तात्पर्य यह है कि यह वो देश है, जिसके पास ये सामर्थ्य रहा था। इसको हम फिर कैसे दोबारा regain करें।" The complete address is available at the PMO website http://pmindia.gov.in/en/news_updates/text-of-the-prime-minister-shri-narendra-modis-address-at-the-ceremony-held-to-rededicate-sir-h-n-reliance-foundation-hospital-and-research-centre-in-mumbai/?comment=disable. Translation is mine.

science have bought into this business of promoting "cultural owner-ship" for the goal of doing good science. [14]

Once we see the "science in the Vedas" discourse for what it is – a fabrication of heritage – three questions arise, which will be examined in the rest of the Introduction. The first question has to do with the relationship between the glorious past and the present state of affairs. Here we will ask if it is really the case that because we were, presum-ably, great in sciences once, we will be great again. The other two ques-tions have to do with how the "scientific" heritage is put together and made to appear reasonable. Here we will examine two favorite ploys of heritage-makers, namely, presentism and parochialism. Let us look at these issues seriatim.

* * *

Let us start with the promise of becoming great "again."

We seem to think that by glorifying our ancient knowledge-tradi-tions, we are providing cultural self-confidence to the present and fu-ture generations of scientists. We seem to think that if we can establish continuity between ancient and modern modes of inquiry, we will gain confidence in our presumably "innate" acumen to do science.

But the notion of continuity between the science of the antiquity – not just the sciences of Indian antiquity, but of *any* ancient civilization

---

14   This group largely includes those scholars who have accepted multiculturalist and relativist view of science wherein modern "Western" science is seen as only one form of science at par with other cultural constructions. This view has become quite pervasive, especially among feminist and postcolonial scholars of science. See Harding 2011, for a recent overview.

Multiculturalism in science assumes that all standards of evaluation of evidence and judgement as to the soundness of a belief are internal to the culture, gender, social class/caste one is born in, and therefore, when students are exposed to mod-ern science they are being asked to embrace culturally alien definitions of nature and standards of judgments. If the students were exposed to science using "their own" cultural vocabulary, they will become better learners and better scientists. Sundar Sarukkai (2014) offers a well-articulated statement of this position.

Based upon my experience first as a young woman trained in microbiology in India, and now as someone who teaches history of science to science students in the Indian Institute of Science Education and Research in Mohali, India, I believe that the cultural relativity of standards of evidence and judgment is overstated.

in the world – and modern science is unwarranted and unproductive. It is unwarranted because it does not acknowledge the *break* from the tradition that happened with modern science. The science that emerged after the Scientific Revolution through the 16th to 18th centuries was a very different enterprise from all earlier attempts to understand nature. Most historians of science [15] agree on the following revolutionary transformations that marked the birth of modern science:

1. Mathematization of nature, i.e. a growing attempt to describe natural things and events in mathematical terms which could be quantified, using increasingly precise tools of measurement (clocks, compasses, thermometers, barometers and such).

2. Fact-finding experiments in addition to direct observations. In the hands of early modern scientists (represented by the paradigmatic figure of Galileo), mathematization of nature was brought together with controlled experimentation.

3. Development of a mechanistic world picture which tried to explain the workings of the natural world in nothing but corpuscles of matter in motion.

4. An uncommon appreciation of manual work, which led to the relative lowering of barriers between university-trained natural philosophers and artisans and craftsmen. [16]

Undoubtedly, this revolution was made possible by a confluence of a multitude of earlier achievements of many civilizations – the ancient Greeks, Christianity, Islam, and through Islam, the contributions of ancient and classical India and China. But the new science that emerged after the Scientific Revolution was most unlike any of the nature-knowledge traditions that went to into it, *including* the Greco-Roman, and Judeo-Christian tradition, that are the *direct* ancestors of the Western civilization. While it took on board some elements of mathematical and observational stock of knowledge from earlier civilizations, modern science – the SaWKiT – turned the ancient cosmos and ancient methods of speculative reason upside down, and produced a new concep-

---

15 At least those historians of science who have not written-off the very idea of a scientific "revolution" as a Western ploy to project its superiority over all others.

16 In two magisterial books, H. Floris Cohen, a Dutch historian of science, has explored the emergence of distinctively modern science. See Cohen, 1994 and 2010.

tion of the cosmos and the humanity's place in it. *So revolutionary and sweeping have the changes been that it is oxymoronic to say that any pre-modern knowledge tradition – be it Hindu, Christian, Islamic, Jewish, Buddhist, Taoist, animistic – had the answer to the questions asked by modern scientists.* Of course the nature of the natural world (its composition, the fundamental laws governing its operations) has not changed, but the conceptual categories, methodological criteria and the aims of inquiry have undergone such a radical transformation that it is safe to say with Thomas Kuhn that the ancients and the modern scientists practically live in different worlds. [17]

If one accepts this picture of the birth of modern science, then the very idea of ancients having the answers that have emerged only in the last 500 years or so makes no sense. Of course, there are nuggets of useful empirical knowledge – the knowledge of useful medicinal plants, or organic methods of farming, for example – that can be incorporated into the modern corpus *provided* they pass the stringent tests that all empirical claims must go through to be deemed "scientific." But beyond that, it is simply vainglorious to claim that modern science is only repeating what the ancients already knew. [18]

Not only is the insistence of continuity between ancient and modern sciences unwarranted, it is entirely unproductive. The conviction that we have always-already known everything that is worth knowing, and that everything we knew is only confirmed – never rejected – by science, has *prevented* us from developing an ethos of honest inquiry. The compulsion to establish harmony with the core of the Vedic worldview has *held back* the progress of science in the past, and will continue to hold us back if we continue to go down this path.

Admitting to being an ignoramus – Latin for "we don't know" – is the first step toward acquiring knowledge. This point has been well-articulated by Yuval Harari in his influential book, *Sapiens:*

---

17 Thomas Kuhn's 1962 masterpiece, *The Structure of the Scientific Revolutions* has revolutionized the study of history of science.

18 The classical Indian statement of this sentiment comes from Swami Vivekananda who in his famous Chicago address insisted that that the discoveries of modern science are only restating "in a more forcible language...what the Hindu has been cherishing in his bosom for ages."

> The Scientific Revolution has not been a revolution of knowledge. It has been above all a revolution of ignorance. The great discovery that launched the Scientific Revolution was the discovery that humans do not know the answers to their most important questions.... Even more critically, modern science accepts that the things we know could be proven wrong as we gain more knowledge. No concept, idea or theory is beyond challenge. [19]

Acknowledging that we do *not* have all the answers, and the answers we do have could well turn out to be all wrong, is what allowed modern science to emerge and flourish in Europe in the early modern era, from the 16th to the 18th century. It was not a matter of some special "Faustian Spirit" that existed only in the West, but rather a coming together of theological justifications for empiricism, political and mercantile interests, technological breakthroughs, along with a regard for manual labor that set the stage for the Scientific Revolution.

This process was by no means smooth. There was resistance from the Church and the Aristotelian professors who controlled the medieval universities. Yet eventually, an awareness emerged that the conclusions of the Greek philosophers (the earth-centered universe, the humoral theory of disease, Aristotle's theory of falling objects) and the Bible (the seven-day Creation, the Great Flood) were incorrect, as they failed to adequately explain the evidence obtained through systematic and increasingly precise observations and controlled experiments. Even though all the pioneers – Copernicus, Vesalius, Galileo, Newton and later, Darwin – were devout Christians working from within the traditional medieval view of the world derived from parts of Greek philosophy and the Bible, they managed to set a process in motion which ended up *overturning* the inherited framework.

What is even more important is that despite religious resistance, the scientific revolutionaries were not so compelled by the forces of tradition that they felt forced to "harmonize" their theories and methods with those prescribed by Aristotle and the Bible: Had that been the case, the new science would have died in its cradle. The Copernican theory of sun-centered universe was not absorbed back into the ancient earth-centered universe of Ptolemy, nor was Darwin's theory of natural selection contorted to make it appear as if it was in harmony with the Bible.

---

19 Yuval Noah Harari, 2011, p. 250-251.

Despite initial condemnation on the part of religious forces, it was the bastions of tradition that had to capitulate to the force of evidence. (Yes, there are creationists among fundamentalist Christians who still believe in the literal truth of the creation story, but they are opposed by the mainstream of Christianity.) The metaphysical speculations of the early natural philosophers eventually had to give way to the experimental method, which involved precise measurement and quantification.

In India, on the other hand, the forces of tradition have managed to overpower and tame any idea that threatened to challenge the essential Vedic outlook of the primacy of consciousness, or spirit. History of Indian science abounds in examples of self-censorship by otherwise fine minds; whenever they perceived a contradiction between the Puranas and the mathematical astronomy of the Siddhantas, for example, some of our well-known astronomers allowed the Puranas to overrule the Siddhantas. Disheartening examples include Brahmagupta in the 7th century opposing Aryabhata's theory of eclipses in favor of Rahu and Ketu, as well as Yajñeśvara Rode in the 17th century "crushing the contradictions" that the Copernican astronomy posed to the Puranic worldview.[20] When confronted with conflicting arguments, our learned men did not stand up for what they knew to true and backed by better evidence. For the most part, they chose to kneel before the Eternal Truths of Vedas and Puranas. The forces of conservatism and conformity have been so deeply entrenched in the system of rituals, social habits, and beliefs that govern our society, that our learned men did not have to be hauled up before an Inquisition (as Galileo was) to force them to renounce what they knew to be true – they did that willingly, on their own volition.

The same compulsion to let the Vedas and Puranas have the last word is evident in how the torch-bearers of the Indian Renaissance co-opted scientific theories of physics and biology. The current crop of heritage-makers, including the Prime Minister and the academics who made the Science Congress so memorable are travelling down the road carved out by two of the most illustrious leader of Indian Renaissance, Swami Dayananda and Swami Vivekananda. Like the two swamis, they

---

20 See Christopher Minkowski, 2001; Robert Fox Young, 2003.

too are intent on picking out those modern scientific ideas and methods that they can then fuse with the Vedas and the Puranas.

If history is any guide, the rhetorical illusion of "harmony" between modern science and traditional views has only served the cause of the orthodoxy in India. Far from being a source of critical thinking that accepts that our holy books, our ancestors, and our traditions could be wrong; far from accepting that the old ways must be given up if they don't measure up to best available evidence, this celebration of "harmony" has only co-opted science into religious dogmas. This road leads not to science, but to pseudoscience – whitewashing pet ideas to make them look as if they are scientific.

* * *

Fabrication of heritage is, thus,s a process of domesticating the past, turning it into stories that serve our purposes today.

Presentism, or anachronism, is how the past is domesticated and history turned into heritage.

Presentism means simply this: to see the past through the lens of the present. It has been called the "fallacy of *nunc pro tunc*" which is Latin for "now for then."[21] In history of science (and intellectual history more generally), presentism works by simply introducing contemporary conceptual categories and aims into the depictions of what the "scientists" of earlier epochs were trying to do.

Professional historians are taught to recognize this fallacy of presentism and are trained to avoid it with all their might. "The past is a foreign country: they do things differently there" is the mantra of professional historians.[22] The objective of history then become to study the past ideas and practices within their own social-cultural milieu.

---

21 David Hackett Fischer, 1970, who goes on to add: [the substitution of now for then is the] "mistaken idea that the proper way to do history is to prune away the dead branches of the past, and to preserve the green buds and twigs which have grown into the dark forest of our contemporary world." P. 135.

22 This is the opening line of *The Go-Between*, a novel by L. P. Hartley, published in 1953. It is also the title of a well-known book by David Lowenthal, the well-known historian whose work on heritage we have already referred to.

While historians shun presentism as best as they can, those who peddle heritage find it indispensable. The whole purpose of fabricating a heritage is to infuse the past with present meanings. This requires that the present be projected back into the past. For our purpose at hand – to understand how history of science is saffronized – we have to understand how conceptual categories available to modern science (genetic science, quantum physics, nuclear energy and such) are read back into the minds of our ancestors. In this book, especially in the final chapter, we will examine the use of resemblances and parallelisms that are deployed to make such projections look reasonable and plausible.

Presentist history is not just bad history; it is dangerous history as well. I agree with Eric Hobsbawm's observation that "the most usual ideological abuse of history is based on anachronism rather than lies." This kind of history, again quoting Hobsbawm:

> is the raw material for nationalist or ethnic or fundamentalist ideologies, as poppies are the raw material for heroin addiction. The past is an essential element, perhaps *the* essential element in these ideologies. If there is no suitable past, it can always be invented....the past legitimizes. The past gives a more glorious background to a present that does not have much to celebrate. [23]

* * *

The other major tool for fabricating a suitable heritage is to cordon off your own past from the rest of the world. I believe there is an absence of a serious and honest comparative perspective in the Hindu nationalist history of science. Or rather, to put a finer point on this statement, the comparative perspective is not entirely absent from their analysis, but it is deeply colored by what can only be called a "jagat-guru complex": invariably, India appears as the giver of science, but never a taker.

While this kind of history might be tonic for the Indian ego, it happens to be bad history. It is bad history for the same reason not stepping outside the boundary of your village limits what you can see and experience. It is bad history because it does not allow you to ask new and interesting questions about social and cultural differences that might

---

23 Eric Hobsbawm, 1997, p. 7, 5.

have made a difference in the trajectories that science and technology followed in different societies.

What I find even more distorting about this kind of Indo-centric historiography is that it fails to see and acknowledge how ideas cross national and cultural boundaries: circulation of ideas did not have to wait for the World Wide Web; it has been a part of human history from the very beginning. I share Joseph Needham's call for taking what he calls an ecumenical view of the world:

> The different civilizations did have scientific interchanges of great importance. It is surely quite clear by now that in the history of science and technology, *the Old World must thought of as a whole.* [24]

Once we see the Old World as an interconnected whole, we have no choice but to see our civilization as one among others bound to them by *mutual* exchange of goods, people and ideas. Ideas were not always radiating *from* India to the rest of the world, but also coming *into* India from the rest of the world. Like every other sister civilization, we were givers and we were takers, with no monopoly on giving.

As the reader will discover in the first three chapters, once we get over our *Jagatguru* complex and see India as one in the network of civilizations, a newer, more complex appreciation of India's achievements begins to take shape.

* * *

Before I conclude this introduction, I would like to share with the readers the story of how I came to write this book.

Sometime in January 2015, immediately following the Science Congress in Mumbai, I received a call from a national weekly magazine (that shall remain unnamed) to write a piece analyzing the historical claims that were made at that venue.

As this was an issue that was on my mind anyway, I immediately got to work. Within a week or so, I sent the magazine not one, but two essays – one on Pythagoras and the other on plastic surgery, genetics etc. For reasons that were never explained, the magazine sat on its hands for three weeks. Naturally, I withdrew the essays from consideration.

---

24 Joseph Needham, 1969, p. 16.

If the editor of the magazine is reading these words, please know I am sincerely grateful to you for *not* publishing those essays!

I realized I had much more to say on these matters than the mere two thousand words that I was limited to for the magazine. I decided to expand my mission and to present an exhaustive analysis of these issues. I proposed the idea to my friend, Asad Zaidi, the publisher of Three Essay Collective. He gave me the green light and I went to work on this book.

The product of my labors is now in your hands.

CHAPTER 1

Who Discovered the Pythagorean Theorem?

1. Introduction

Poor Pythagoras! That gentle vegetarian[1] mystic-mathematician would have never imagined that over 2,500 years after his time, hearing his name would have the same effect on some Indians as showing a red rag has on a bull!

At the Indian Science Congress earlier this year, Pythagoras and his theorem were mentioned by many very important persons who went out of their way to make him look like an imposter basking in the lime-light that rightfully belongs to us, the brainy Indians. It is not that Pythagoras doesn't need to be taken down a notch or two, for the evidence that he was the original discoverer of the theorem named after him is simply not there. But that does not by itself mean that the vacated pedestal now belongs exclusively to our own Baudhāyana and his fellow priest-artisans who used ropes to build geometrically complex Vedic altars. And yet, this is exactly what was clearly and repeatedly asserted at the Science Congress.

Here is what the Minister of Science and Technology, Dr. Harsh Vardhan had to say on the matter:

---

1 For reasons that continue to puzzle historians, Pythagoras, who abstained from meat-eating, hated beans. The "Pythagorean diet" was bean-free, as well as meat and fish free. His followers had to swear to follow this diet.

Our scientists discovered the Pythagoras theorem, but we gave its credit to the Greeks. We all know that we knew *bijaganit* much before the Arabs, but selflessly we allowed it to be called Algebra. …whether related to solar system, medicine, chemistry or earth sciences, we have shared all our knowledge selflessly…

The Minister was backed by Dr. Gauri Mahulikar, a Sanskrit scholar from Mumbai University:

In the *Śulvasutras*, written in 800 BCE, Baudhāyana wrote the geometric formula now known as Pythagoras theorem. It was written by Baudhāyana 300 years before Pythagoras…."[2]

Between the two of them, the Minister and the Professor proved a theorem dear to the Indian heart, namely: we are not just brainy, but big-hearted as well. We are so big-hearted that we let the likes of Pythagoras to claim priority for what our own Baudhāyana accomplished. We are so big-hearted that we selflessly give away our intellectual riches – from the geometry of Śulvasūtras to advanced mathematical and medical concepts – to the rest of the world. Giving is in what we do.

Compared to the rest of the howlers at the Science Congress – the ancient interplanetary flying machines, the alchemist cows turning grass into gold, for example[3] – the priority-claim for Baudhāyana has at least one virtue: it is not entirely insane. There is a substantial nugget of truth hidden in an Everest of hype.

There is no doubt that our *śulvakaras* had indeed mastered the Pythagorean conjecture thoroughly and used it in ingenious ways to create Vedic altars of different areas, while conserving the shapes. They were the *first to state it unambiguously*. But they were neither alone, nor the first in having this understanding. The *first recorded evidence* for this conjecture dates back to some 1800 years BCE and it comes from Meso-

---

2   See http://www.thehindu.com/news/national/science-congress-lauds-feats-of-ancient-india/article6754106.ece. The priority of ancient priest-craftsmen who composed the *Śulvasūtras* over Pythagoras has a long history. As early as 1906, Har Bilas Sarda was cheering for Baudhāyana over Pythagoras in his book, *Hindu Superiority*, pp. 286-287. More recently, Subhash Kak has claimed that the geometry of the Vedic altars contains – in a coded form – advanced astrophysical knowledge such as the exact length of the tropical year and the lunar year, the distance between the sun and the earth, the distance between the moon and the earth in lunar diameters. See Kak, 2005.

3   *India Today* has very helpfully listed these howlers. See http://indiatoday.intoday.in/story/5-howlers-from-the-indian-science-congress/1/411468.html.

potamia, the present day Iraq. The *first proof* comes from the Chinese, preempting the Euclidean proof by a couple of centuries, and the Indian proof by at least 1000 years. Even though Pythagoras was not the first to discover and prove this theorem, it does not diminish his achievement. He remains an extremely influential figure not just for history of mathematics, but history of science as well. Pythagoras and his followers were the "first theorists to have attempted deliberately to give the knowledge of nature a quantitative, mathematical foundation".[4] Giants of the Scientific Revolution, including Johannes Kepler and Galileo Galilei walked in the footsteps of Pythagoras.

In this chapter, we will start with a quick refresher on the Pythagorean Theorem. We will follow this with a straightforward narrative of the different formulations and uses of this theorem, starting with ancient Egypt and Mesopotamia, followed by ancient Greece, India and China. The order is not chronological, and nor does it represent a chain of transmission. While we have evidence of the Greeks getting their start in geometry from the Egyptians and the Mesopotamians, it is quite likely that this conjecture was independently discovered in India and China.

The idea of following the trail of the Pythagorean Theorem from Mesopotamia to China is simply to place ancient India as one among other sister civilizations. It is only through a comparative history of the idea behind this famous conjecture that we will be in a position to judiciously assess India's contribution.

2. What is the Pythagorean Theorem?

Before proceeding any further, let us be clear on what the Pythagorean Theorem is all about. Most of us learnt it in middle or high school, but it is a good idea to quickly review it.

The theorem simply states that in a right-angle triangle, the square on the hypotenuse is equal to the sum of the squares on the two sides. (A hypotenuse, to joggle your memory, dear reader, is the longest side of a right-angle triangle which also happens to be the side opposite the right angle).

---

4   G.E.R. Lloyd, 1970, p. 26.

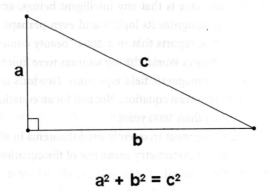

$$a^2 + b^2 = c^2$$

Figure 1

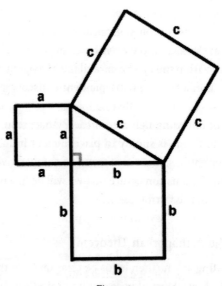

Figure 2

In figure 1, c is the hypotenuse, while a and b are short and long sides of the right angle triangle, respectively.

So the theorem simply states the following

$c^2 = a^2 + b^2$, a relationship that is represented in figure 2.

This theorem seems simple and intuitive. That is why it has been nominated as a calling-card for the human species to be beamed into the outer space.[5] The idea is that any intelligent beings, anywhere in the universe, would recognize its logic – and even perhaps be moved by its beauty. Eli Maor reports that in a 2004 "beauty contest" organized by the journal *Physics World*, the top winners were Euler's formula, Maxwell's four electromagnetic field equations, Newton's second law, followed by the Pythagorean equation. Not bad for an equation that has been around for more than 3000 years.[6]

It is also one of the most frequently used theorems in all of mathematics. Algebra and trigonometry make use of the equation. Its most obvious and practical use is in the building trade, where it is used for constructing walls perpendicular to the ground, or for constructing perfect squares or rectangles.

This use follows from the fact that the theorem is *reversible* which means that its *converse* is also true. The converse states that a triangle whose sides satisfy $a^2 + b^2 = c^2$ is *necessarily* right angled. Euclid was the first (1.48) to mention and prove this fact. So if we use lengths which satisfy the relationship, we can be sure that the angle between the short and the long side of a triangle will have to be right angle.

Any three whole numbers that satisfy the Pythagorean relationship and yield a right angled triangle are called *Pythagorean triples*. The most obvious and the easiest example of these triples is 3, 4, 5. That is to say:

$3^2 + 4^2 = 5^2$ or

$9 + 16 = 25$.

That means that any triangle with sides 3, 4 and 5 will be a right-angle triangle. As we will see in the rest of this chapter, this method for building right-angle structures was known to *all* ancient civilizations, not just India. This method is still used by carpenters and architects to get a perfect perpendicular or a perfect square.[7]

---

5   In his classic work of science fiction, *From the Earth to the Moon* (1865), Jules Verne mentions a German mathematician who suggested that a team of scientists go to Siberia and on its vast plains, set up an enormous, illuminated diagram of Pythagorean theorem so that inhabitants of the Moon would see that we are trying to get in touch. Verne's un-named mathematician has been identified as Carl Friedrich Gauss. See Eli Maor, p. 203.

6   Maor, p. xii.

7   If you want to construct a perfect square and you don't have anything but a tape measure and a marker try this: draw a straight line roughly 3 units long where you

While all right-angle triangles will bear the relationship described by $c^2 = a^2 + b^2$, not all a and b lengths can be expressed as whole numbers or as ratios of whole numbers. You can see it for yourself: try calculating c for a=4 and b=5, or a=7, b= 9. In both cases, you will see that the c cannot be expressed as a whole number. Actually there are only 16 set of whole numbers below 100 that fit into the Pythagorean equation.

There is one particular number for a and for b that puzzled all ancient civilizations that we have records from. That number is one. Imagine a square with side measuring one unit. Now draw a diagonal cutting the square into two right angle triangles.

The simple question is this: how long is the diagonal?

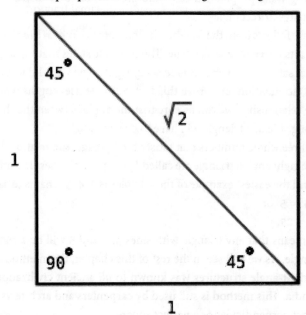

Let us see:
For a right angle triangle, we know that
$$c^2 = a^2 + b^2$$

---

want to locate the corner of the square. On the other side of the corner, draw a line 4 units long, roughly vertical to the first line. Now use the tape to make sure that the edges of the two lengths are exactly 5 units apart. The angle between the two corner lines will be exactly 90 degrees.

In this case,

$c^2 = 1^2 + 1^2$

$c^2 = 2$, therefore $c = \sqrt{2}$

If you recall your middle-school mathematics, the $\sqrt{}$ symbol stands for square root. Square root of a number is simply a value which, when multiplied by itself, gives that number.

In the above case, in order to find how long the hypotenuse is, we have to find out square root of two, or in other words, find out that number which, when multiplied with itself will produce the number 2.

Try figuring out the square root of number 2. You will notice something strange: you simply cannot express the number as a fraction of two whole numbers. What you find is that the decimal fractions of the number that will give you 2 when multiplied by itself simply go on and on, without ending and without repeating themselves. For practical purposes, square root of 2 is taken to be 1.4142136 but the number can go on forever.

Numbers such as these were given the name "alogon" by the Greeks which means "unsayable or inexpressible". We call them *irrational numbers*.

Irrational numbers were known to all the ancient civilizations that are examined in this chapter. All of them tried to represent these numbers by using rough approximations. Only among the Greeks, however, it led to a crisis of spiritual dimensions. We will shortly explain why, and what they did about it. But we have to start our story from the beginning in Egypt and Mesopotamia.

3. Egypt and Mesopotamia

If anyone can take credit for being the first to figure out the Pythagorean Theorem, they have to be the unknown and unnamed builders, land-surveyors, accountants and scribes of ancient Egypt and Mesopotamia (the land we know as Iraq today) sometime between 2000 to 1700 BCE.

Just as ancient India had its *śulvakaras* who used a length of rope to map out altar designs, ancient Egypt had its *harpedonaptai*, the "rope stretchers". If Herodotus, the Greek historian who lived in the fifth century BCE is to be trusted, these rope-stretchers were surveyors sent out by the pharaohs to measure the farm land for tax purposes every time the river Nile would flood and change the existing boundaries. They are rightly considered the true fathers of geometry, which literally means measurement (*metery*) of earth (*geo*): they were the land surveyors sent out by the pharaohs to measure the land for taxation purposes everytime the river Nile would flood and change the existing boundaries.

One would think that a civilization that built the Great Pyramids[8] would have mastered the right-angle rule and much-much more. Indeed, it has been claimed by Martin Bernal in his well-known book, *The Black Athena,* that the Greeks learned their sciences and mathematics from Egypt, with its roots in Black Africa. This is not the right forum to resolve this huge controversy, but Bernal's claims regarding the advanced state of mathematics and astronomy in Egypt have been challenged, and are no longer held to be credible by most historians.[9]

The two main mathematical papyri – the Ahmes Papyrus (also called the Rhind Papyrus) that dates back to 1650 BCE and the so-called Moscow Mathematical Papyrus that contains text written some 1850 BCE – don't make any reference to this theorem. While both these papyri contain geometrical problems like calculating the areas of squares, volume of cylinders (for the jars they stored grain in), circumference and areas of circles, the familiar Pythagorean relation is not there. Yet it is hard to imagine how the pyramid makers could have laid the foundations of the square base of pyramid without the familiar 3, 4, 5 rule described in the previous section.

A more recent find has thrown new light on this issue: the so-called Cairo Mathematical Papyrus, which was unearthed in 1938 and contains materials dating back to 300 BCE shows that the Egyptians of this, much later era, did know that a triangle with sides 3,4,5 is right-angled,

---

8 The best known of them, the Great Pyramid at Gizeh, built around 2600 BCE was the largest building of the ancient world. It rose 481 feet above the ground, with four sides inclined at an angle of 51 degrees with the ground. Its base was a perfect square with an area of 13 acres – equal to the combined base areas of all the major cathedrals in all of Europe. Some 400,000 workers labored on it for 30 years. Burton, 2011, p. 58.

9 See the important paper by Robert Palter (1993) titled, 'Black Athena, Afro-centrism and the History of Science'.

as are triangles with sides 5, 12, 13 and 20,21,29. This papyrus contains 40 problems of mathematical nature, out of which 9 deal with the Pythagorean relationship between the three sides of a right triangle.[10]

We may never get the complete story of Egyptian mathematics, as the ancient Egyptians wrote their texts on scrolls made out of flat strips of pith of the papyrus reeds that grew abundantly in the marshes and wetlands of the region. The problem with papyrus is that it is perishable.

But the Mesopotamian civilization that grew not too far away from Egypt on the fertile land between the rivers Tigris and Euphrates in modern-day Iraq is a whole different story in so far historical records go. The clever Sumerians, Assyrians and Babylonians who successively ruled this land have left us a huge library of their literary and mathematical works chiseled on clay tablets which were dried in the sun (and often baked in accidental fires) and are practically indestructible.

As in Egypt, the Mesopotamian mathematics and geometry grew out of administrative needs of the highly centralized state. Temples of local gods and goddesses also needed to keep accounts of the gifts and donations. This led to the flourishing of many scribe-training schools where men (they seem to be all men) learned how to write and do elementary arithmetic. Fortunately for historians, the Mesopotamian people chose a non-degradable material – wet clay that their rivers brought in plenty – to write upon. They used a reed with an edge – quite like our *kalam* – that could make wedge-shaped marks on the clay. These tablets were then dried in the sun which made them practically indestructible.[11] Literally thousands of these clay tablets have been recovered and deciphered, including the famous Flood Tablet which tells the story of a great flood, very similar to the Biblical story of the flood and Noah's Ark.

A small fraction of the tablets recovered from schools for scribes contain numerical symbols which were painstakingly deciphered by Professor Otto Neugebauer at Brown University, USA in the 1930s. It is now well-established that the Babylonian people had developed a pretty

---

10 Burton, 2011, p. 78.

11 Clay tablets were also recyclable: if a scribe made an error, he could simply knead his tablet into a ball and make a fresh tablet out of it.

ingenious system that allowed them to use just two symbols – a wedge for the number one and a hook-shaped symbol for the number ten – to represent and manipulate any number, however large. They could do that because they had figured out what is called place value, in which the value of a number changes with the position it occupies. What is more, they also started using a symbol indicating empty space – a forerunner of zero. (Place-value and zero will be examined in the next chapter).

But what is of special interest to us are two tablets which have an iconic status in history of mathematics, namely, Plimpton 322 and a tablet called YBC7289 housed in Columbia and Yale universities, respectively. These tablets reveal that the Mesopotamians knew how to figure out Pythagorean triples, and could also calculate square roots. Some historians conjecture that Plimpton might even be the first record of trigonometry anywhere in the world.[12]

Wikipedia provides a very good description of Plimpton 322:

> Plimpton 322 is partly broken clay tablet, approximately 13 cm wide, 9 cm tall, and 2 cm thick. New York publisher George Arthur Plimpton purchased the tablet from an archaeological dealer, Edgar J. Banks, in about 1922, and bequeathed it with the rest of his collection to Columbia University in the mid-1930s. The tablet came from Senkereh, a site in southern Iraq corresponding to the ancient city of Larsa. The tablet is believed to have been written about 1800 BC, based in part on the style of handwriting used for its cuneiform script.

A line-drawing of Plimpton 322 (Figure 4a) and a transcript of cuneiform numerals into modern numbers (Figure 4b) are given below. What is written on it that makes it so important? It has four columns of numbers and it appears that there was a fifth column on the left which broken off. The first column from the right is simply a column of serial numbers, from 1-15, while the other three columns contain 15 numbers written in Cuneiform script.

What do these columns of numbers mean? This tablet was first deciphered by Otto Neugebauer and his colleague Alfred Sachs in 1945. Without going into details which can now be found in any standard text book of history of mathematics, they concluded that "the numbers b and d in the second and third columns (from right to left) are

---

12 "If the missing part of the tablet shows up in the future.... Plimpton 322 will go down as history's first trigonometric table." Eli Maor, 2007, p. 11.

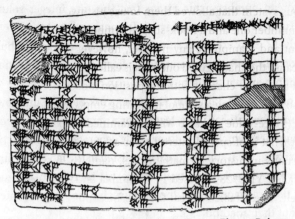

Figure 4a. Line drawing of Plimpton 322. Source: Eleanor Robson at http://www.dma.ulpgc.es/profesores/pacheco/Robson.pdf

	Width	Diagonal	
1:59:00:15	1:59	2:49	1
1:56:56:58:14:50:06:15	56:07	1:20:25	2
1:55:07:41:15:33:45	1:16:41	1:50:49	3
1:53:10:29:32:52:16	3:31:49	5:09:01	4
1:48:54:01:40	1:05	1:37	5
1:47:06:41:40	5:19	8:01	6
1:43:11:56:28:26:40	38:11	59:01	7
1:41:33:45:14:03:45	13:19	20:49	8
1:38:33:36:36	8:01	12:49	9
1:35:10:02:28:27:24:26	1:22:41	2:16:01	10
1:33:45	45	1:15	11
1:29:21:54:02:15	27:59	48:49	12
1:27:00:03:45	2:41	4:49	13
1:25:48:51:35:06:40	29:31	53:49	14
1:23:13:46:40	56	1:46	15

Figure 4b. Transcription of the Plimpton 322 tablet using modern digits. Source Clark University, Department of Mathematics and Computer Science http://aleph0.clarku.edu/~djoyce/mathhist/plimpnote.html¬)

Pythagorean numbers, this means that they are integer solutions to $d^2=b^2+l^2$ where d and b stand for the diagonal and the leg of the triangle respectively."[13] To use modern terminology, the numbers tabulated in Plimpton 322 are Pythagorean triples, which as defined in section 2, are whole numbers that fulfill the Pythagorean relation, $a^2+b^2=c^2$.

In other words, Plimpton 322 is the work of some unknown Babylonian mathematician, or a teacher or a scribe trying to find sets of whole numbers which will automatically generate a right angle. What is most striking is that some of the triples listed in the tablet are simply too large for a random, hit-and-trial discovery.[14] There are many guesses as to how they managed to get these values, but nothing definite can be said about their method.

The second tablet that has received great amount of scrutiny is called YBC 7289, making it the tablet number 7289 in the Yale Babylonian Collection. The tablet dates from the old Babylonian period of the Hammurabi dynasty, roughly 1800-1600 BCE.

This celebrated tablet shows a tilted square with two diagonals, with some marks engraved along one side and under the horizontal diagonal. A line-drawing of the tablet and a sketch in which the cuneiform numerals are written in modern numbers is given below (Figures 5a and 5b on the next page):

The number on the top of the horizontal diagonal when translated from the base-60 of Mesopotamians to our modern 10-based numerals, gives us this number: 1.414213, which is none other than square root of 2, accurate to the nearest one hundred thousandth. The number below the horizontal diagonal is what we get on multiplying the 1.414213 with the length of the side (30) which, in modern numbers comes to 42.426389. This tablet is interpreted as showing that the Mesopotamians knew how to calculate the square root of a number to a remarkable accuracy.

These two tablets are the first evidence we have of the knowledge of what we today call Pythagorean Theorem.

---

13 Otto Neugebauer, p. 37.
14 For example, row 4 has the following triples 12,709 (the short side), 18,541 the hypotenuse, and 13,500 the third side of a right angle triangle. See Katz, p. 20.

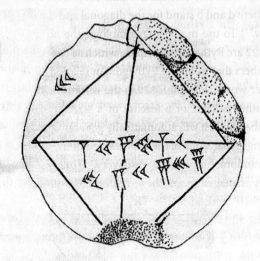

Copyright: A. Aaboe

Figure 5a. Line-drawing of the Yale tablet, YBC 7289.
Source: Mathematical Association of America.

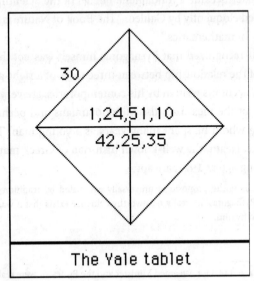

Figure 5b. YBC 7289 transcribed into modern numerals. Source: McTutor History of
Mathematics Archives at http://www-history.mcs.st-andrews.ac.uk/index.html

4. Pythagoras, the Pythagoreans and Euclid

Pythagoras (about 569 BC-about 475 BC) is perhaps the most misunderstood of all figures that have come down through history. We all know him as the man who gave us the theorem that – rightly or wrongly – bears his name. But for Pythagoras and his followers, this theorem was not a formula for doubling the square or building precise perpendiculars, as it was for all other civilizations of that time. It is a safe bet that neither Pythagoras nor his followers ever lifted a length of rope, got down on their knees to measure and build anything, for that kind of work was seen fit only for the slaves.

The real – and path-breaking – contribution of Pythagoras was the fundamental idea that *nature can be understood through mathematics.* He was the first to imagine the cosmos as an ordered and harmonious whole, whose laws could be understood by understanding the ratios and proportions between the constituents. It was this tradition that was embraced by Plato, and through Plato became a part of Western Christianity, and later became a fundamental belief of the Scientific Revolution expressed eloquently by Galileo: "The Book of Nature is written in the language of mathematics."

It is well-recognized that Pythagoras himself was *not* the original discoverer of the relationship between three sides of a right-angled triangle. Greek accounts written by his contemporaries are very clear that Pythagoras got the idea from the Mesopotamians and perhaps Egyptians, among whom he spent many years as a young man. The words of Sir Thomas Heath, the well-known historian of Greek mathematics, written as long ago as 1921, are apt:

> Though this is the proposition universally associated by tradition with the name of Pythagoras, no really trustworthy evidence exists that it was actually discovered by him.[15]

---

15 Heath, 1921, p. 144. Our esteemed Minister and the Professor were really tilting at windmills. Greeks have always admitted that they learned their geometry from Egyptians and Mesopotamians. All serious historians of mathematics would agree with Sir Heath's words.

Neither is there any clear-cut evidence that Pythagoras or his followers offered a proof of the theorem. Those who attribute the proof to Pythagoras cite as evidence stories about him sacrificing a number of oxen when he proved the theorem. Apparently the story about oxen being sacrificed comes from a writer by the name of Apollodorus. But as Thomas Heath has argued, the passage from Apollodorus does mention the sacrifice without mentioning *which* theorem was being celebrated. The sacrifice story has been challenged on the grounds of the Pythagoreans' strictures against animal sacrifices and meat-eating.[16]

The first Greek proof of the theorem appears in Euclid's classic of geometry called *Elements*, which was written at least three centuries *after* Pythagoras. Euclid (around 365 BCE-275 BCE) provides not one, but two proofs of this theorem – theorem 42 in Book I, and theorem 31 of the Book VI. Nowhere does Euclid attribute the proofs to Pythagoras.[17]

Why then did this theorem get Pythagoras' name? No one knows for sure. It is possible that Greeks were following a tradition of attributing new ideas to well-recognized sages – a practice that is very common in Indian scientific and spiritual literature as well. Pythagoras, after all, was no ordinary man: he had a semi-divine status among his followers.

While he did not discover it or prove it, this equation played a most dramatic – one can say, catastrophic – role in Pythagoras' confidence in mathematics and numbers. To understand the catastrophe, one has to understand the fundamental place numbers and ratios occupied in the Pythagorean view of the world.

Pythagoras was a mystic-mathematician, a cross between "Einstein and Mrs. Eddy" to use Bertrand Russell's words.[18] Or one can say that he was a mystic with a mathematical bent of mind. He saw contemplation of mathematical proportions and ratios as the highest form of meditation that can bring the mind in tune with the Ultimate Reality that he

---

16 Heath, 1921, pp. 144-145.

17 The first proof, I:42, is generally attributed to Eudoxus, who was a student of Plato, while the second proof is attributed to Euclid himself. See Eli Maor, chapter 3.

18 Mrs. Mary Baker Eddy founded a spiritualist movement called Christian Science in 1879. The quotation is from Russell's well-known *History of Western Philosophy*, p. 31.

believed existed independently of material stuff. What is more, he believed that mathematical knowledge can purify the soul and free it from the cycles of rebirth. (Yes, his spiritual beliefs overlapped with the belief system prevalent in India. More on this below).

Pythagoras was born in 571 BCE (which makes him a rough contemporary of Gautam Buddha in India and Confucius in China) on the island of Samos in the Aegean Sea, just off the coast of modern-day Turkey. He spent many years of his youth in Egypt and later in Mesopotamia. In both places, he immersed himself in the spiritual and mathematical traditions of the host cultures. There is no evidence that he travelled as far east as India, but there is a strong possibility that he picked up the belief in immortality of the soul and its reincarnation from Hindu teachers who were probably present in the courts of Persian kings before Alexander opened a direct line between India and Greece when he came as far as the Indus river in 326 BCE. It was his belief in reincarnation that led him to oppose eating meat and stick to a bean-free vegetarian diet – a dietary practice which is as un-Greek today, as it was then. Like the Hindus, he believed in purification of the soul through contemplation of the Ultimate Reality in order to break the chain of rebirth – except that for him, mathematics was the form that the contemplation of the Ultimate took.[19]

Could he not have picked up the geometry of Baudhāyana and other śulvakaras as well who are estimated to have lived anywhere between 800-300 BCE? It is entirely possible, although the Greek historians of that time have left no record of it. The same historians, on the other hand, have left meticulous records of what he learned from Mesopotamians and Egyptians.

But wherever Pythagoras learned this theorem from, it played a unique role in his philosophy. It led to the discovery of *irrational num-*

---

19 For pre-Alexandrian contacts between Indians and Greeks, see McEvilley, 2002, ch. 1. The possibility of Pythagoras learning his beliefs in immortality and rebirth of the soul from Indian philosophers is accepted by many scholars. See Kahn 2001 and McEvilley,2002 for example. One of the many stories that are told about Pythagoras is that he once stopped a man from beating a dog by telling him that he recognized the dog as an old friend, reincarnated. His followers believed that Pythagoras could recall many of his earlier births and that was one reason they treated him as a divine man.

bers (see section 2) which led to a great spiritual crisis for himself and his followers. To understand why a mathematical result would lead to a spiritual crisis, some background is needed.

While we don't have any evidence for Pythagoras discovering the Pythagorean Theorem, his role in discovering the laws of musical sounds is well-attested. It appears that one day as he was walking past a blacksmith's workshop, he was intrigued by the sounds coming from within. So he went in to investigate and found that the longer the sheets of metal that were being hit by the blacksmith's hammer, the lower was the pitch of the sound. When he came back home, he experimented with bells and water-filled jars and observed the same relationship: the more massive an object that is being struck or plucked, the lower the pitch of the sound it produces. He experimented with strings and observed that the pitch of the sound is inversely proportional to the length of the string that is vibrating. He figured out that if a string is plucked at a ratio of 2:1 it produces an octave, 3:2 produces a fifth, 4:3 a fourth.

This was a pivotal discovery – of far greater importance to Pythagoras than the famous theorem he is known for. It made him realize that human experience of something as subjective as music could be understood in terms of numerical ratios: the quality of what pleases the ear was determined by the ratios of the lengths that were vibrating. This was the first successful reduction of quality to quantity, and the first step towards mathematization of human experience.[20]

The realization that what produces music are certain numerical ratios led Pythagoras to derive a general law: that *the ultimate stuff out of which all things are made are numbers*. Understand the numbers and their ratios and you have understood the Ultimate Reality that lies behind all phenomena, which you can only see in your mind, not through your senses. If all is number – and numbers rule all – then obviously, we should be able to express that number either as whole numbers (integers like 2, 6, 144 etc.) or as fractions of whole numbers (for example, half can be written as one divided by two).

Given how central numbers and numerical ratios were to Pythagoras's view of the unseen reality which humans could access through

---

20 This interpretation is from Arthur Koestler's well-known book, *The Sleepwalkers*.

mathematics, one can understand that the discovery that square root of two cannot be expressed as either a whole number or a fraction of two whole numbers would lead to an unprecedented crisis.

This discovery was a direct result of the Pythagorean Theorem. Here is what happened: having understood the right-angled triangle relationship (i.e., $a^2+b^2=c^2$) either Pythagoras himself or one of his students tried use it to calculate the diagonal of a square whose side is one unit. They discovered that they simply can't get to a definite number that would terminate somewhere. In other words, they realized that some lengths cannot be expressed as a number. This shattered their fundamental belief that all is number and the ratio of numbers can explain the order of the cosmos.

The legend has it that Pythagoras swore his followers to complete secrecy regarding this awful discovery: they were never to disclose the existence of irrational numbers to anyone. One unfortunate follower by the name of Hippasus who broke the vow of secrecy was pushed to his death from a boat into the Mediterranean Sea – so the story goes.

The crisis led to further developments in Greek mathematics. To begin with, it led to a split between geometry and arithmetic. For Pythagoras, all numbers had shapes. But irrational numbers could not be expressed in shapes. The existence of irrationality was proven later by Aristotle and Euclid.

To conclude this section: yes, Pythagoras was not the original discover of this theorem. But he put it to a different use than it was anywhere else. The truly important discovery of Pythagoras was not the famous theorem, but the laws of music and the existence of irrational numbers.

5. Śulvasūtras

We now come to the central theme inspired by the Minister and the Professor mentioned earlier. To recapitulate, they asserted that what the world knows as the Pythagorean Theorem should be renamed after Baudhāyana who discovered it in 800 BCE, which is nearly 200 years before Pythagoras was even born.

As we have already seen, this claim is factually incorrect: there is a great amount of evidence chiseled into the Mesopotamian clay that proves that Pythagoras was *already* outdone before even Baudhāyana was born! But if we let go of this madness for who came first, we will see that Baudhāyana and his colleagues who lived and worked somewhere between 800 to 500 BCE (or between 600-200 BCE, according to some estimates[21]) were extremely creative artisans-geometers in their own right. Their accomplishments don't need to be judged from the Pythagorean or the Greek lens.

What are these *Śulvasūtras* that we keep hearing about? Who composed them? When? Why? These are some of the questions we will try to answer in this section.

As mentioned earlier, *śulva* means a cord or string, while *sutras* are short, poetic sentences that are easy to memorize. These "sutras of the cord" are a part of the *kalpa*-texts that make up one of the six Vedangas, or limbs of the Vedas, each dealing with a specialized topic ranging from grammar to astronomy. The *kalpa* literature specializes in ritual matters, including building of fire altars, or *vedis*, some of them very intricate in shapes and sizes.

The most succinct definition is provided by George Thibaut, the German philologist who first translated these sutras:

> The class of writings, commonly called *Śulvasūtras* means the "sutras of the cord". *Śulvasūtras* is the name given to those portions or supplements of the *Kalpasūtras* which treat of the measurement and construction of different *vedis*, or altars, the word *śulva* referring to the cords which were employed for those measurements. I may remark at once that the sutras themselves don't make use of the word *śulva*; a cord is regularly called by them *rajju* (rope).[22]

Out of four extant texts, the two most important are those by Baudhāyana and Āpastamba. Next to nothing is known about these men, but "most likely they were not just scribes but also priest-craftsmen, performing a multitude of tasks, including construction of the

---

21 Agathe Keller (2012) dates Baudhāyana to 600 BCE.
22 Thibaut 1992[1875], p. 417. George Thibaut is an interesting figure in Indology. He was born in Germany in 1848 and later moved to England to work with Max Muller. In 1875 he became a professor of Sanskrit at Benares Sanskrit College. It was here that he produced his studies on the *Śulvasūtras*. But his real claim to fame was his work on mimamsa texts. See Keller, 2012, pp. 261-262.

*vedi*s, maintaining *agni* and instructing worshippers on appropriate choice of sacrifices and altars."[23]

If it was the need for repeated measurements of land in the flood-zones of rivers that gave birth to geometry in Egypt and Mesopotamia, it was the need for precision in Vedic rituals that gave birth to geometry in India. In order for the Vedic yagnas to bear fruit, they had to be carried out precisely according to the guidelines laid out in the Brahmana texts of *Yajurveda*: the mantras had to be recited just so, the sacrificial animal quartered exactly at specific vertebra, the altar (*vedi*) for the sacrifice had to be constructed exactly following the prescribed shapes and sizes. Thus, ritual has been recognized as the source of sciences and indeed, by some, of all civilization.[24] Let us see how the need for exactness in ritual led to advances in geometry in ancient India.

To begin with, the shape of the altar was decided by the goal of the yagna. For example those who desired to go to heaven were required to construct a falcon (*syena* in Sanskrit)-shaped *vedi* because as *Taittirīya Saṃhitā* explained: "the falcon is the best flyer among the birds; and thus he (the sacrificer) having become a falcon himself flies up to the heavenly world."[25] For those seeking food, the altar should be in the shape of a trough (called *drona-cit*), while those seeking victory over the enemy were to build an altar in the shape of a *rathachakra* or a wheel.

What is geometrically challenging about these requirements is this:

- To use Thibaut's words: "every one of these altars had to be constructed out of five layers of bricks... every layer was to consist of 200 bricks [arranged in such a manner] that in all five layers, one brick was never lying upon another brick of the same size and form."
- If this wasn't challenging enough, *the area of every altar, whatever its shape* – falcon with curved wings, wheel, tortoise,

---

23 George G. Joseph, p. 327.

24 A. Seidenberg, 1962, proposes that *civilization itself* has its origin in rituals. We will discuss the contribution of the ritual horse sacrifice (Ashvamedha yagna) in understanding equine anatomy in ancient India in chapter 3.

25 Thibaut, p. 419.

trough etc. – had to be equal to $7^{1/2}$ square *purusha*, where a *purusha* is the height of a man with uplifted arms.[26]

- There was yet another challenge: every-time the sacrifice was carried out after the first construction and consecration, the area had to be increased by one square *purusha*, until one comes to the one-hundred-and-a-half-fold altar. As Seidenberg explains, "the sacrificer is [symbolically] climbing a ladder, his sacrificial rank being determined by, or determining, the area."[27]

- Here comes the most daunting challenge of all: while the area had to be increased by one square *purusha* at each subsequent construction, *the relative proportions of the single parts had to remain unchanged.* In other words, area was to be increased while preserving the shape of the altar.

- There is another twist to altar-making which shows the deep roots of the varna order: If the *yajman*, or the host of the yagna, was a Brahmin, he was required to set up the sacred fire at eight units east of the household fire, if a prince, eleven and the Vaisya twelve.[28]

Clearly, constructing such altars was no mere "carpentry problem", to use Seidenberg's words, that could be solved with a few "carpenter's rules".[29] The technical problems were not trivial, for as Thibaut puts it:

Squares had to be found which would be equal to two or more given squares, or equal to the difference of two given squares; oblongs had to be turned into squares and squares into oblongs; triangles had to be constructed equal to given squares and oblongs and so on....[Even for the most ordinary of *vedi*s] care had to be taken that the sides really stood at right angles, for would the *āhavaniya* fire have carried up the offerings of the sacrificer to the gods if its hearth had

---

26 It is not entirely clear how this man of one-*purusha* height is chosen. Is he any average sized man, or the *yajman* hosting the yagna?

27 Seidenberg, 1962, p. 491.

28 Kim Plofker, p. 24. Plofker calls these units "double-paces where a pace equals 15 angulas". An angula or digit is said to be equal to 14 grains of millet.

29 Seidenberg is right in poking fun at those Hellenophiles who treat any tradition of geometry that does not justify itself through a Euclidean deduction as merely "carpentry".

not the shape of a perfect square?... [there were also occasions when] a square had to be turned into a circle of the same area.[30]

The most important arsenal in the mental tool-kit of the altar-makers was what we call Pythagorean Theorem.

Baudhāyana gave a very close approximation to this theorem, even though he used four-sided right-angled structures rather than the right-angled triangle that we are familiar with. Here are three sutras (1.9-1.13) from Baudhāyana Śulvasūtras which capture the essence of this theorem, one for the diagonal of a square and another for the diagonal of an oblong or rectangle, followed by Pythagorean triples:

> 1. "The cord which is stretched across in the diagonal of a square (sama-catu-rasra) produces an area of double the size."

That is: the square of the diagonal of a square is twice as large as the area of the square.

> 2. a. "The cord stretched on the diagonal of an oblong (dirgha chaturasra) produces both areas which the cords forming the longer and the shorter side of an oblong produce separately."

That is: the square of the diagonal of an oblong is equal to the square on both of its sides. This is an unambiguous statement of the Pythagorean theorem.

> 2. b. "This (2a) is seen in those oblongs the sides of which are 3 and 4, 12 and 5, 15 and 8, 7 and 24, 12 and 35, 15 and 36."

Here, Baudhāyana is enumerating five Pythagorean triangles, that is, right-angled triangles whose sides will yield a hypotenuse, which when squared will yield twice the area of the two sides which have the dimensions described in 2a. All three sides of the resulting triangles can be expressed in whole numbers.[31]

The numbers in 2b are none other than our old friends, the Pythagorean triples. We encountered them first on Plimpton 322 which dates back at least a thousand years before Baudhāyana. The Pythagoreans not only knew about the triples, but had actually worked out a formula

---

30 Thibaut, pp. 420-421.
31 Thibaut, p. 422-424.

for finding these triples.[32] So we can say that Baudhāyana was no less than his contemporaries, but *he was not ahead of them either.*

Once these insights were acquired, it became easy to conduct many operations required for altar construction. Thus, doubling the area of a square became a breeze: all you had to do was to figure out the diagonal of the existing square and construct a square on it. Or you could easily triple the size of a square by building an oblong on the diagonal of the second square obtained by doubling the first square.

We also find these principles at work in the construction of a *vedi* for the *soma* ritual described by Āpastamba. If one follows Āpastamba's instructions described by Thibaut, it becomes obvious that the altar-makers were using cords and pegs in the ratio of what we would call Pythagorean triples (5, 12, 13) to construct the east and west side of the *vedi* at right angles on the axis of the *vedi* running through the center.[33]

There is lot more to these sutras than just the first enunciation of Pythagoras theorem. Of special interest is the discovery of a procedure for calculating the square roots. The need for calculating the square roots emerged for the same "irrationality" that so bothered the Pythag-oreans. The problem is that the diagonal of any square is incommensu-rable with the length of the sides. This creates a problem for someone who is trying to calculate the diagonal of a square, knowing its sides. We find in Baudhāyana an approximate method of finding square roots, and using this method we get a fairly accurate square root of two to the fifth decimal place.[34] Here again, our *śulvakaras* were in good company: the Yale tablet shows the Babylonians knew how to solve the square root of 2 problem, and the Greeks nearly had a mental breakdown over it!

We now come to the controversial matter of proof. For a long time, the mathematical traditions of ancient India and China have been put down as merely "carpenter's rules" which lack proof, while the only

---

32 The Pythagoreans figured out formulas for calculating triples for an odd number and an even number. These formulas were later given a proof by Euclid. See Katz, p. 38-39 for details.

33 Thibaut, pp. 424-426.

34 See Thibaut, pp. 430-431 and Joseph, pp. 334-336 for details. Thibaut provides useful explanations of how *śulvakaras* could square a circle, build a falcon shaped altar and other complex altars.

valid model of proof that is admitted is that modeled on Euclid that proceeds through deductions from first principles. It is true that the authors of *Śulvasūtras* only meant to convey, in short memorable sutras, how to construct the altars. As a result, they did not try to explain how they arrived at their methods. But that does not mean that the later Indian commentators on these sutras did not feel the need to "remove confusion and doubts regarding the validity of their results and procedures; and to obtain consent of the community of mathematicians."[35] The Greeks were not the only ones to feel the itch to justify their theorems, albeit the deductive method of proof was unique to them.

Even though Baudhāyana and other *śulvakaras* don't provide a proof, later texts do. The first Indian proof of the insights regarding right angle and diagonals was provided by Bhaskara who lived in the 12th century.

6. "Was Pythagoras Chinese?": the Kou-Ku theorem

Sometime in the 6th century BCE when Pythagoras and his followers were working out their number-based cosmology in islands around the Aegean Sea, when *Śulvasūtras* were being composed in India, the Chinese, too, had figured out the Pythagorean theorem. Not only that, they had also given an elegant proof for it. Later they would call it *kou-ku* theorem, which is sometimes also referred to as *gou-gu* theorem.

The first reference and proof of this theorem appears in the oldest mathematical text known in China. It is called *Chou Pei Suan Ching* which translates into *The Arithmetical Classic of the Gnomon and the Circular Paths of Heaven*. Just as in the case of *Śulvasūtras*, the exact date of this text is not known. To quote from Frank Swetz and T.I.Kao, authors of *Was Pythagoras Chinese?*:

> While the exact date of its origin is controversial, with estimates ranging as far back as 1100 BCE, it can generally be accepted on the basis of astronomical evidence that much of the material in the book was from the time of Confucius, the sixth century BCE and its contents would reflect the mathematical knowledge accumulated in China until that time.[36]

35　Srinivas 2008, p. 1833.
36　Swetz and Kao, 1977, p. 14.

Chou Pei is largely devoted to using the gnomon to measure the length of the shadow of the sun.[37] But the first part is devoted to the properties of right-angle triangles. This part consists of a dialogue between Chou Kung (the ruler of Chou) and a wise man by the name of Shang Kao who "knows the art of numbering". Chou Kung wants to know how the astronomers could have "established the degrees of the celestial spheres?" He is puzzled because as he says, "there are no steps by which one may ascent to heavens, and the earth is not measurable by a footrule. I should like to ask you what is the origin of these numbers?"

Shang Kao explains that the art of numbering originates from "the circle and the square. The circle is derived from the square and square from a rectangle." What follows is a statement of what would later be given the name of *kou-ku* theorem:

> let us cut a rectangle diagonally and make the width (*kou*) 3 units, and the length (*ku*) 4 units. The diagonal (*ching*) between the two corners will then be 5 units long.[38]

This statement is immediately followed with a proof:

> after drawing a square on this diagonal, circumscribe it by half-rectangles like that which has been left outside, so as to form a square plate. Thus the four outer half-rectangles of width 3, length 4 and diagonal 5, together make two rectangles (of area 24); then, when this is subtracted from the square plate of area 49, the remainder is of area 25. This process is called piling up the rectangles (*chi chu*).

> The methods used by Yu the Great[39] in governing the world were derived from these numbers.

> Chou Kung exclaimed "great indeed is the art of numbering. I would like to ask about the Tao of the use of right-angle triangle."

---

37 Gnomon is a primitive form of a sun-dial. Mesopotamians are known to have used it, the Greeks are known to have borrowed it from Mesopotamians. Indian astronomers knew it as *shanku*.

38 Notice the familiar triples 3, 4, 5.

39 According to Needham (1959, p. 23), "the legendary Yu was the patron saint of hydraulic engineers and all those concerned with water-control, irrigation and conservancy. Epigraphic evidence from the later Han, when the *Chou Pei* had taken its present form, shows us, in reliefs on the walls of the Wu Liang tomb-shrines the legendary culture-heroes Fu-Hsi and Nu-Kua holding squares and compasses. The reference to Yu here undoubtedly indicates the ancient need for mensuration and applied mathematics."

After Shang Kao explains the "Tao of the use of right-angle triangle",[40] the dialogue ends with Kao declaring:

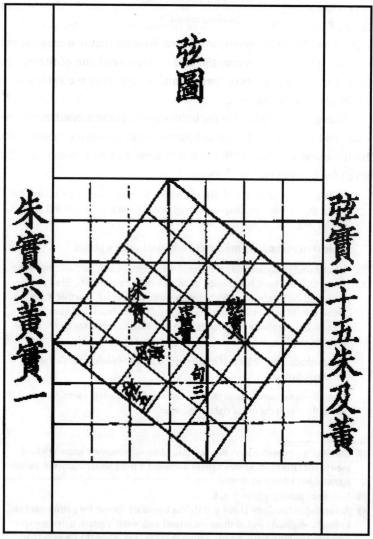

Figure 6. Hsuan-Thu is considered the earliest proof of Pythagoras Theorem, dating back to around 600 BCE.

---

40 Which is nothing more than rules for using a T-square.

He who understands the earth is a wise man and he who understands the heavens is a sage. Knowledge is derived from a straight line. The straight line is derived from the right angle. And the combination of the right angle with numbers is what guides and rules ten thousand things.

Chou Kung exclaimed: "Excellent indeed."[41]

This dialogue is accompanied by a diagram (figure 6 on page 44). This is what is called *hsuan-thu* and is considered one of the earliest and most elegant proofs of the hundreds of proofs of the Pythagorean theorem that exist today.[42]

This proof is relevant to the Indian story. As mentioned in the previous section, *Śulvasūtras* did not provide any proof of the theorem and the first Indian proof appears in the work of Bhaskara in the 12th century.

Some historians believe that Bhaskara's proof is influenced by this ancient Chinese proof. This was first pointed out by Joseph Needham who writes:

> Liu Hui [see below] called this figure 'the diagram giving the relations between the hypotenuse and the sum and difference of the other two sides, whereby one can find the unknown from the known.' In the time of Liu and Chao, it was colored, the small central square being yellow and the surrounding rectangles red. The same proof is given by the Indian Bhaskara in the +12th century.
>
> The *Hsuan thu* proof of the Pythagoras theorem given in the +3rd century commentary of Chao Chun-Ching on the *Chou Pei* is reproduced exactly by Bhaskara in +12the century. It does not occur anywhere else.[43]

This proof is often confused with Pythagorean proof. But this proof shows an arithmetical-algebraic style of the Chinese which was totally alien to the Greek geometry which abstracted ideal forms from numbers. As Needham puts it, the classic passage from *Chou Pei* quoted above:

> ...shows the Chinese arithmetical-algebraic mind at work from the earliest times, apparently not concerned with abstract geometry independent of con-

---

41 The complete dialogue can be found in Swetz and Kao, pp.14-16, and also in Needham.

42 For a simple explanation of this proof that even those without much mathematical aptitude (including myself) can understand, see http://www.mathisfun.com/geometry/pthagorean-theorem-proof.html

43 Needham and Wang Ling, 1959, p. 96 and p. 147. This position is supported by Swetz and Kao, p.40, and also finds support from Victor Katz, pp. 240-241.

crete numbers, and consisting of theorems and propositions capable of proof, given only certain fundamental postulates at the outset. Numbers might be unknown, or they might not be any particular numbers, but numbers there had to be. In the Chinese approach, geometrical figures acted as a means for transmutation whereby numerical relations were generalized into algebraic forms.[44]

This theorem shows up again in the 9th chapter of the most well-known ancient classics of mathematics in China, called *Chiu Chang Suan Shu*, which translates as *Nine Chapters on the Mathematical Art*. This work was composed in the Han dynasty (3rd C. BCE). The version that survives to the present is a commentary by Liu Hui in 250 CE. Liu Hui has the same iconic stature in China as Aryabhata has in India.

The ninth chapter of the book is titled "Kou-ku" which is an elaboration, in algebraic terms, of the properties of right-angle triangles first described in *Chou Pei*.

Why kou-ku or gou-gu? To cite Swetz and Kao, in a right angle, the short side adjacent to the right angle is called *kou* or *gou* (or "leg"). The longer side adjacent to the right angle is called *ku* or *gu* (or "thigh"). The side opposite to the right angle (the hypotenuse) is called *hsien* (or "bowstring").[45]

This chapter contains some kou-ku problems that are famous around the world for their elegance and the delicately drawn sketches that accompany them. These include the so-called "broken bamboo problem" and "the reed in the pond problem". Both of these problems, it is claimed, found their way into medieval Indian and European mathematics texts. The "reed in the pond" problem appears in Bhaskara and the "broken bamboo" in the 9th century Sanskrit classic *Ganit Sara* by Mahavira.[46]

One thing that the Chinese and the Indian geometers shared – and what set them apart from the Greeks – was that geometry never got

---

44 Needham and Wang Ling, 1959, pp. 23-24.

45 Swetz and Kao, pp. 26-28.

46 Swetz and Kao, pp. 32-33 for the "reed in the pond" problem, pp. 44-45 for the "broken bamboo" problem. See also Needham, p. 147.

Not having training in mathematics, I am not in a position to render my independent judgement. But there are striking similarities between Li Hui's (250 CE) reed problem and Bhaskara's (12th century) Lotus problem. See Swetz and Kao for detailed statement of the problem in both cases.

linked to spiritual and/or philosophical questions, as it did in Greece. It remained more of an art used for practical matters. But that does not mean that their ideas were not supported by arguments and spatial manipulation (as in the *Hsuan-thu* proof). Just because these proofs did not follow Euclid's axiomatic-deductive methods, does not make them any less persuasive.

7. Conclusion

This chapter has followed the trail of the so-called Pythagoras Theorem through centuries, crisscrossing the islands on the Aegean Sea, and traveling through the river valleys of the Nile, the Tigris and the Euphrates, the Indus and the Ganges, and the Yellow River. We have looked at the archeological evidence left behind on Mesopotamian clay tablets and on Egyptian and Chinese scrolls. We have examined the writings of the Greeks and the sutras of our own altar-makers. We have wondered at the achievements of the ancient land-surveyors, builders and mathematicians.

Having undertaken this journey, we are in a better position to answer the question: "Who discovered the Pythagorean Theorem?" The answer is: the geometric relationship described by this theorem was discovered independently in many ancient civilizations. The likely explanation is that the knowledge of the relationship between sides of a right-angle triangle emerged out of practical problems that all civilizations necessarily face, namely, land measurement and construction of buildings – buildings as intricate as the Vedic fire altars, as grand as the Pyramids, as functional as the Chinese dams and bridges, or as humble as simple dwellings with walls perpendicular to the floor.

Where is India in this picture? Indian *śulvakaras* were one among the many in the ancient world who hit upon the central insight contained in the Pythagorean Theorem: they were neither the leaders, nor laggards, but simply one among their peers in other ancient civilizations. *Our* Baudhāyana need not displace *their* Pythagoras, as they were not running a race. They were simply going about their business, Baudhāyana and his colleagues concentrating on the sacred geometry of fire altars, Pythagoras and his followers worrying about the ratios and proportions that underlie the cosmos.

It is merely an accident of history, undoubtedly fed by the Eurocentric and Hellenophilic biases of Western historians, that the insight contained in the theorem got associated with the name of Pythagoras. Apart from shoring up pride in our civilization, nothing much is to be gained by insisting on a name change. The correct response to Eurocentrism is not Indo-centrism of the kind that was on full display at the Mumbai Science Congress. The correct response is to stop playing the game of one-upmanship altogether.

The itch to be The First is unproductive for many reasons. For one, it turns evolution of science into a competitive sport, history of science into a matter of score- keeping and the historians of science into referees and judges who hand out trophies to the winner. The far greater damage, however, is inflicted on the integrity of ancient sciences and their practitioners whose own priorities and methods get squeezed into the narrow confines of the Greek achievements.

If we really want to honor Baudhāyana and other śulvakaras, a far more sincere and meaningful tribute would be to understand their achievements in the totality of their own context, including the ingenious methods they employed for solving complex architectural problems. Viewing ancient Indian geometry purely, or even primarily, through the lens of Pythagoras actually does a disservice to Baudhāyana, for there is lot more to Śulvasūtras than this one theorem.

It is high time we freed ourselves from our fixation on Pythagoras. Let him Rest in Peace.

Chapter 2

Nothing That Is: Zero's Fleeting Footsteps[1]

जब ज़ीरो दिया मेरे भारत ने,
भारत ने, मेरे भारत ने,
दुनिया को तब गिनती आई।
तारों की भाषा भारत ने,
दुनिया को पहले सिखलाई।

देता ना दशमलव भारत तो,
यूँ चाँद पे जाना मुश्किल था।
धरती और चाँद की दूरी का,
अंदाज़ लगाना मुश्किल था।[2]

1. The question

Indians of a certain age grew up humming this ditty from the 1970 Hindi film, *Purab aur Paschim*. Judging by the hits it gets on YouTube, it seems as if the song continues to tug at Indian heartstrings even today, almost half-a-century after it was composed.

The lyrics resonate because they affirm what is already imprinted in our national psyche. It is drilled into our heads by school teachers, religious teachers, family elders, Bollywood films, and politicians, that

---

1 The title of this chapter is inspired by books by Robert Kaplan (1999) and Lam Lay-Yong (2004).

2 The movie's title, *Purab aur Paschim* translates into "East and West." Here is a rough translation of the lyrics: Only after my Bharat (India) gave zero, could the rest of the world learn how to count; my Bharat first taught the world the language of the stars. Had Bharat not given the decimal system to the world, it would have been difficult to reach the moon, or even to calculate the distance between the earth and the moon.

zero and the decimal system are India's unique and revolutionary contributions to world mathematics and science. Countless books and essays are written by Indian mathematicians and historians that declare
zero to be an "entirely Hindu" contribution to world mathematics.[3] The
sentiment expressed in the song – that if it were not for the genius of ancient Bharat, the world wouldn't have known how to count – is widely
shared. If there is one "fact" in history of science that is assumed to be
true beyond any reasonable doubt, it is the Indian origin of zero.

But is this really true? Is it *really* irrefutably established that ancient
India was the original source of the number zero and the decimal numbering system that is the foundation of modern mathematics?

This is the question that this chapter seeks to answer.

2. Two principles and a hypothesis

Two principles will guide this chapter.

The first is a commitment to comparative history. Comparative
history simply means studying ideas, institutions, and historical processes across different socio-cultural systems separated by space and/or
time. Histories that can be compared can exist within the same nation
(the structure of family in Kerala and Punjab, for example), across na-
tions (historical trajectories of economic growth in China and India, for
example) or across civilizations (the philosophies of nature in ancient
Greece and India at a comparable time period, for example). Comparative history can produce valuable insights for identifying events/pro-
cesses/institutions that could have set a society on a certain trajectory

---

3   The classic in this genre is Bibhutibhusan Datta and Avadesh Singh's *History
of Hindu Mathematics* published in 1938. This strain of "out of India" writing
continues in academic circles, including elite science and engineering institutions, see Datta, 2002, for example. Prestigious scientific institutions routinely host
ideologues with scientific credentials who make hyperbolic claims about Hindu
origins of zero (and just about every landmark in history of science) backed by
nothing more than Sanskrit *shlokas*, randomly selected and idiosyncratically
interpreted. For a recent example, see the lecture by Dr. N. Gopalakrishnan, the
founder-director the Indian Institute of Scientific Heritage at IIT-Madras recently.
(The lecture can be seen at https://www.youtube.com/watch?v=Kv41pJT7500).
Books like Dr. Priyadarshi's *Zero is not the Only Story* continue to gain traction in
the public sphere, including places like IIT-Kanpur.

which may differ from other societies in direction or in pace. Only by comparison can historians get to understand whether the developments in question are unique to a society, or are part of a much broader movement.[4]

Cross-civilizational comparisons are of special relevance in history of science, especially when scientific achievements are appropriated for nationalistic purposes and cast in the following form: " the civilization Y was the first to come up with the idea X." Replace Y with "ancient Indian mathematicians/scientists-sages" and X with zero and decimal system, or with any other notable scientific discovery, and we get exactly the kind of history of science that is being propagated in India today.

The very idea of being "the first" is an inherently comparative idea: unless there are others engaged in a similar project, how can there be a "first"? Can there be a winner in a marathon without there being a marathon? To crown any civilization Y the "first" to come up with X, requires us to see what Y's sister-civilizations A, B, or C were doing in the domain of X.

It is true that there has been a long tradition of history-writing that simply assumed that the European civilization – with its birth in ancient Greece and its coming of age in Christianity – gave birth to everything of value. This kind of history suffers from a serious bout of Hellenophil-

---

4   According to Karl Marx, "Events strikingly similar but occurring in a different historical milieu, lead to completely different results. By studying each of these evolutions separately, and then comparing them, it is easier to find the key to the understanding of this phenomenon; but it is never possible to arrive at this understanding by using the passe-partout [master-key] of some universal-historical theory whose great virtue is to stand above history." Quoted from Raymond Grew, 1980, p. 766. Marc Bloch, another master of comparative history, has emphasized the importance of the comparative method as a means of systematically gathering evidence to test the validity of explanations of historical changes. As William Sewell (1967,p.208-209) writes in his exposition of Bloch's work, "if an historian attributes the appearance of phenomenon A in one society to the existence of condition B, he can check this hypothesis by trying to find other societies where A occurs without B, or vice versa. If he finds no case which contradict his hypothesis, his confidence in its validity will increase…. If he finds contradictory evidence, he will either reject the hypothesis outright or reformulate and refine it so as to take into account the contradictory evidence and then subject it again to comparative testing." Clearly, historical comparisons serve a function that is very similar the role of experiments in natural sciences.

ia, which David Pingree has described as "a kind of madness" caused by the delusion that the only real sciences are those that began in Greece and then spread to the rest of the world. On this account, Europe is the sole Giver, while the rest of the world is merely a passive Receiver.[5]

Eurocentric history is deeply flawed and condescending to the rest of the world. Yet, an uncritical and self-celebratory Indo-centric history is nothing but a mirror image of uncritical and self-celebratory Eurocentrism: Both are equally illogical and equally chauvinistic. What we instead need is an appreciation that independent mathematical and scientific developments can cross cultural barriers, take root and blossom in many different kinds of soils.[6]

The second principle that will guide this chapter is that history of even as abstract a subject as mathematics cannot be understood without paying close attention to the "counter-culture" of mathematics, that is, the practical manipulation of numbers using movable counters, be they clay tokens, pebbles, sticks, or beads on an abacus. Most histories of mathematics tend to focus exclusively on the written number-records while completely ignoring number-manipulations using counters. Moreover, most histories of mathematics are histories of "pure" mathematics which, in the ancient world, was invariably intertwined with the quest for the divine (the Pythagorean number mysticism, construction of altars and temples for ritual purposes, for example. See Chapter 1). What these standard histories overlook is the history of practices – counting, computing, measuring, weighing – that ordinary people in

---

5   David Pingree, 1992, p. 555. See also George G. Joseph's important book, Crest of the Peacock, for a critique of what he calls "classical Eurocentrism" in history of mathematics.

While Eurocentrism is obviously problematic, anti-Eurocentric histories often have the feel of flogging a dying horse. Thanks to the sustained post-colonial critiques and equally sustained self-critiques by European and North-American scholars, history of science has moved away from an uncritical Hellenophilia of the earlier generations, and has made significant strides toward a more inclusive and context-sensitive historiography. Even a cursory glance at the educational curricula in the US schools and universities will show that Europe is by no means treated as the center of the known universe. Today, it is not Eurocentrism, but romantic multiculturalism that poses a greater danger to the study of history of science because of its potential to foster ethnocentrism and nativism.

6   This formulation is from Joseph, 2011, p. 12

all cultures developed for taking care of their ordinary material needs. Simple practices like keeping track of sheep in a herd, trading, collecting taxes, and building houses, bridges, dams, temples etc. all required some methods for manipulating numbers. Once we pay attention to such practices, a whole another dimension is added to the historical search for the origin of zero.[7]

Once these two principles are applied to available evidence, two new ways of understanding the evolution of zero, and India's role in it, begin to emerge:

a. When the Indian evidence is placed alongside the evidence from other civilizations of comparable development, it becomes clear that the Indian contributions were neither unique, nor without precedent. Evidence presented in this chapter will show that the Hindu-Arabic system of numeration involves no principle that was not already familiar to India's sister civilizations. All the elements that went into the creation of zero – counting by powers of ten, decimal place-value, and the concept of empty space in the decimal ranking – were well-known for many centuries in many diverse cultures before they all came together in India in the form that we use today.[8] Indian mathematicians further developed zero as a number like any other number which could be used in arithmetical operations. All of these are substantial contributions for which India is justly admired. But the claims of India being the one and only civilization to arrive at zero as a mathematical concept are simply not substantiated by the historical evidence taken in its totality.

---

7   The idea of "counter-culture" and the distinction between "number manipulation" and "number recording" are from the important work of Reviel Netz (2002). Netz makes a powerful case for writing history of numeracy and even literacy from the perspective of computational practices: "The rule is that across cultures, and especially in early cultures, the record and manipulation of *numerical symbols* precede and predominate over the record and manipulation of *verbal symbols*.... In other words, *in early cultures, numeracy drives literacy, rather than the other way around*," p. 323. A similar point has been argued by Sal Restivo (1992). Both see the *practices of counting and manipulating numbers* as more fundamental than the *practices of recording numbers* in texts.

8   There is a substantial literature on Tamil and Sinhalese numerals. See Georges Ifrah, 2000, for details. We will, however, focus only on the Brahmi-Nagari numerals, as they are the ancestors of the modern Hindu-Arabic numerals.

b. secondly, when the sources of evidence are widened beyond metaphysical speculations to include every-day, practical counting and computing practices of ordinary people, a new window opens up which faces East of India, to China and South-East Asia. The window- opener is the renowned historian of Chinese science, Joseph Needham (aptly described as "the man who loved China") who, along with his Chinese colleagues produced the monumental multi-volume work *Science and Civilization in China* which is considered a landmark in comparative history of science. In the third volume of this massive work, Needham and his co-author, Wang Ling, propose a Chinese origin of zero as a number, which they say travelled from China, through Southeast Asia to India where it acquired the familiar form that the whole world uses today. In their own words:

> ... the written symbol for nil value, emptiness, sunya, i.e., the zero, is an Indian garland thrown around the nothingness of the vacant space on the Han counting boards.[9]

A very similar thesis has been put forward in recent years by Lam Lay Yong, a renowned historian of mathematics based in National University of Singapore. In her various writings which culminated in her book titled *Fleeting Footsteps*, Lam has argued that "the Hindu-Arabic numeral system had its origin in the Chinese rod-numeral system."[10] Lam supports Needham's thesis that it is through Southeast Asia, "where the eastern zone of Hindu culture met the southern zone of the culture of the Chinese" that the practice of using empty space in the process of counting and doing basic arithmetic crossed over from China into India where it acquired the shape that the whole world is familiar with.[11]

---

9   Needham and Wang Ling, 1959, p. 148. Simon Winchester's recent biography of Needham is titled *The Man who Loved China*.

Joseph Needham (1900-1995) was a British biochemist who became fascinated with the Chinese language which he learnt from his Chinese students at Cambridge University. (He would marry one of these students much later in life after his first wife passed away). He spent extended periods of time in China, travelling and studying.

10 Lam Lay Yong and Ang Tian Se, 2004: 170. Professor Lam was the recipient in 2002 of the Kenneth O. May medal, the highest honor in history of mathematics.

11 Needham and Wang Ling, 1959, p. 148.

The Needham-Lam thesis will be examined in greater details in this chapter. By bringing China into the story of zero, my intention is not to start another Indo-Chinese race. Instead, my motivation is to de-nationalize the way we write history of science in India. Needham's well-known work on Chinese mathematics has been around since the 1960s, while Lam Lay Yong has been publishing her work since the 1990s to great acclaim by professional historians. While this thesis is gaining wide acceptance and is making its way into well-known textbooks, we in India have remained oblivious to it.[12] Most Indian historians of mathematics (with the exception of George Joseph's *Crest of the Peacock*) that do touch upon India-China cultural exchanges start with the assumption that India was the Giver and China was the grateful Receiver of not just Buddhism, but of everything else of value in mathematics and sciences.[13] Does this assumption of unilateral flow of mathematical ideas from India to China, Southeast Asia and later, through the Arab mathematicians, to the rest of the world hold up against the best available historical evidence? The chapter will try to answer this question.

Before we get into the historical details, some clarity about the mathematical concepts of decimal base, place value and zero is called for.

3. The preliminaries: numbers, decimal, place-value and zero

It is quite common in Indocentric histories to find zero indiscriminately grouped with decimal counting and decimal place value – and all three given an Indian birth-certificate. The problem is that the three concepts did not evolve together: presence of decimal counting systems don't necessarily imply the knowledge of decimal place value, albeit the knowledge of place value was a pre-requisite for the evolution of zero.

---

12 See Victor Katz's (2009) well-known text book on history of mathematics.

13 For example, R. C. Gupta's (2011) paper on Indian contributions to Chinese mathematics starts with this totally unhistorical statement: "the countries in East Asia received with Buddhism not only their religion but *practically the whole of their civilization and culture.*" p. 33, emphasis added. Such a stance clearly devalues centuries of pre-Buddhist achievements of ancient China.

Unless we un-bundle them and understand each on its own terms, we simply can't understand their evolution.

To begin with, the word "number" is more complicated than we give it credit for. Numbers obviously count things, but they are not the things themselves; you can pick up two cups, or two of anything, but you can't pick up the number "two". "Two" is an abstraction, an idea in our heads. It does not exist by itself.[14]

There are two ways all cultures seem to have for expressing numbers. The first is through "number words" which can be spoken or written in the local language. For example, a Sanskrit speaker would use the word शतम् (shatam) to mean 100, an Arabic speaker would call it مائة/مِائَة (mi'a) while a Greek would call it Hekaton.

The other way to represent numbers is through the use of symbols. The symbols can be of two kinds. The first kind are what are called "numerals" which are simply marks representing numbers. Our own Hindu-Arabic 1,2,3... 9 and 0 are the most obvious example of numerals. But the markings that are used for representing numbers have varied through history and cultures. For example, ancient Babylonians represented the number one hundred using Cuneiform symbols, while Greeks would write the Greek letter ϱ (" rho") to write their number-word Hekaton. We don't know what numeral the composers of the Vedas would have used to represent shatam or any other Sanskrit number-word, because we don't have any written records of Sanskrit numerals.[15] The first numerals we find in India are written in Kharosthi and Brahmi and date back only to 300 BCE. In the modern world, however, peoples of all countries throughout the world understand and use the Hindu-Arabic number-symbols, or numerals – the familiar 1,2,3.... Even though different cultures continue to use number words in their own local language (ek, do, teen in Devanagari; ena, dio, tria in Greek), the Hindu-Arabic numerals are now universally understood and used. (We will look at the evolution of Hindu numerals from Brahmi later).

---

14 See Ian Stewart, 2007, p. 9.

15 The numerals used in Sanskrit today are Devanagari numerals which date back to the Gupta period (200-550 CE).

The second kind of symbols use words which symbolize number words. Referred to as *Bhūta-sankhyā* in medieval Sanskrit mathematical texts, this way of representing numbers is also called "object numbers" or "concrete numbers". Rather than use number word or numerals, this system makes it possible to express any number by the name of whatever object – real or mythical – that routinely occurs in that number. Thus, the number two can be represented by all the Sanskrit words for "eyes" because eyes naturally come in pairs. The symbols can also come from religious texts and ritual practices: thus the word "agni" can stand for number three, as there are three ritual fires; "anga" can stand for the number six, as there are six limbs of the Vedas. Alberuni, writing around the turn of the first 1000 years after the Common Era, describes this system thus:

> ... [for] each number, Hindu astronomers have appropriated quite a great quantity of words. Hence if one word does not suit the metre, you may easily exchange for a synonym which suits. Brahmagupta says: 'if you want to write one, express it by everything that is unique, as the earth, the moon; two, by everything that is double e.g., black and white; three by everything which is threefold; the naught by heaven, the twelve by the names of the Sun.[16]

This unique way of recording numbers arose out of the compulsion to write mathematical and astronomical ideas in verse so that they could be easily memorized. Our mathematically-minded poets faced a problem; it wasn't easy to use number-words in verse all the time. They needed synonyms which would sound better and be easy to remember. These terse sutras were committed to memory, while the guru directly explained the full meaning to the students. Commentaries in prose were written to expound on the meaning of the symbols and the sutras.[17]

The point is this: you can record, versify, and memorize number-words and concrete symbols, but you cannot compute with them. (Try

---

16 Alberuni in Sachau 1971, p. 177.

17 There is a vast literature on the preference for orality and the influence it had on development of sciences in India. For mathematics, see Yano, 2006, Plofker, 2009, Filliozat, 2004. Ifrah believes that this system is unique to India (p. 409) and also provides an extensive list of number symbols (p. 499).

adding "*chakshu-akaash-agni*" to "*ashvin-anga-pitamaha*", or, even better, try multiplication or division!).[18]

Let us turn to the term "decimal". According to the Oxford English Dictionary, the word decimal simply means: "a system of numbers and arithmetic based on the number ten, tenth parts, and powers of ten." This simply means counting by power of tens, or bundling by tens.

Counting by tens is the result of the fact that human beings have ten fingers. Earliest records show that numbers beyond one and two evolved by addition – three by adding two and one; four as two and two, and so on. As commerce and crafts developed, the need for larger numbers grew. This led to the bundling of numbers first in fives as in ‖‖, and later the base 10. With 10 as the base, larger numbers could be constructed by addition or subtraction (12 is 10 plus 2, 20 is 10 plus 10, and 19 as 20 minus 1 etc.) and by multiplication (20 is 2 times 10 etc.). Some civilizations (the ancient Mayans) used 20 as the base (fingers and toes), while for reasons that are not clear, ancient Mesopotamians used 60 as the base. As we will see in the next section, base 10 or decimal system of counting, did not originate in India: it is simply the most common method of counting and cuts across civilizations.

You can have a *decimal system of counting* without a zero, but you cannot have *decimal place value* without having a symbol for an empty place or what we today call zero. In other words, the existence of decimal counting itself does not constitute evidence for zero; but a decimal place value does. While 10-based or *decimal counting* is almost universal and has been around from the very beginnings of civilization, *decimal place value* is another story altogether.

What is place value? Place value, also called positional notation, has been described as "one of the most fertile inventions of humanity, comparable to the invention of the alphabet which replaced thousands of picture-signs."[19] In the place-value method of writing numbers, *the position of a number symbol determines its value*. Consider the number 211 written in our modern decimal notation: the numeral 1 has the

---

18 Hint: the numbers are 302, and 162, as the number symbols are read from right to left.

19 Otto Neugebauer, 1962, p. 5.

value of one if it occupies the first place from the right, but the same 1 stands for a ten as it moves one place to the left. Similarly, 2 is not simply the sum of one and one, but has the value of two-hundred. If the order changes, the value changes; for example, 112 is a very different number from 211.

Consider a larger number: 4567. If we stop to think about it, this number is actually made up of the following: 4x1000 + 5x100 + 6x10 + 7x1. In other words, every position from right to left is a multiple of 10 (unit, 1 is one tenth of 10, tens (10x1), hundred (10x10, or 10^2), thousand (100x10, or 10^3) and so on to millions, billions, trillions, etc. If we accept this rule, then instead of explicitly spelling out the powers – four thousand, five hundred, sixty seven, we simple assume that in this case, 4 is to be multiplied by 10^3, 5 by 10^2 and so on.

The beauty of place value – and the reason it is considered revolutionary – is that it allows you to write any number, however large or small, with just a few numerals. Using the modern decimal system, nine digits (1 to 9) and a zero are sufficient to write any number without having to invent new symbols for each digit of a number, or for each multiple of the base 10.

If the place value notation did not exist, separate symbols would be required for writing 10, 20,30, ... 90 and for 200, 300 ... 900. Let us take an example. We know from the existing evidence (which will be examined in more details in later sections), that in India place-value notations first made their appearance around the time of Asoka around 300 BCE, while the ancient Greeks never developed it at all. Thus, someone living before the Asokan era in India would write the number 456 (for example) in Brahmi by using a symbol for 400, followed by a separate symbol for 50, followed by a symbol for six. Similarly, his Greek counterpart would write the same number as υνς, where these letters from the Greek alphabet stand for 400, 50 and 6 respectively. To contrast, in a positional value notation (in our example 456), the numeral 4 would stand for 400 (4 units at the 100th position), five would stand for 50 (five units at 10th position) and six for 6 units. In other words, the order in which the numerals are written or spoken would automatically indicate whether they represented a thousand, hundred etc. In this system, the work of "power words" – special words or signs indicating numerical rank (thousand, hundred, tens etc.) – is simply transferred to the places any of the first 9 numerals occupy.

We can now understand fully what Neugebauer meant when he said that the invention of place value notation is analogous to the creation of the alphabet. Inventing place value meant that the thousands of separate symbols that were needed to represent individual numbers became obsolete, just as the alphabet rendered hieroglyphics obsolete. Instead of memorizing large number of symbols, just the nine digits (1 to 9) plus a sign for empty space – the familiar, somewhat oval-ish empty circle we call zero – are enough to write any number however big or small.

What does place value notation have to do with zero?

The answer: *Zero was born out of place value notation.* To be more precise, place value is *necessary* for the evolution of zero as a numeral, but it is *not sufficient*, for you can have place value without a zero if you have number words that are larger than the base. For example, you could write or say 2004 as "two thousand and four", without using a zero. But if you are writing in numerals, you cannot write 2004 without indicating that there is nothing under tens and hundreds – and zero is what indicates the absence of any number, or the presence of nothing. Without some way of indicating nothing, the numerals 2 and 4 could well mean 24 or 204. As Georges Ifrah put it in his well-known book, *The Universal History of Numbers:*

> In any numeral system using the rule of position, there comes a point where a special sign is needed to represent units that are missing from the number to be represented... It became clear in the long run that *nothing* had to be represented by *something.* The something that means nothing, or rather the sign that signifies the absence of units in a given order of magnitude is ...[what we call zero.][20]

As the above example shows, the philosophers and scribes who used *number words* could get by without having a special numeral that indicated nothing. But it is also important to note that the need for zero was not obvious to those who practiced everyday mathematics in their daily lives either. As Alfred North Whitehead put it, "the point about

---

20 Georges Ifrah, 2000, pp. 149-150. Emphasis in the original.

zero is that we do not need to use it in the operations of daily life. No one goes to buy zero fish." Charles Seife, whose book this quote is taken from, goes on to add, "you never need to keep track of zero sheep or tally your zero children. Instead of 'we have zero bananas,' the grocer says, "we have no bananas. *We don't have to have a number to express the lack of something.*"[21]

It is only when numbers are written as numerals or as number-symbols in a positional order, does the need for a zero emerge. In other words, when 10-based numerals began to be arranged according to their rank, the symbol for zero became necessary.

4. The evidence

In popular discourse, the Indian origin of zero has become an article of faith: it has acquired the status of an established fact which is beyond any doubt. For professional historians of mathematics, however, the Indian origin story remains a puzzle, with many unsolved elements. As Kim Plofker, the author of the well-received *Mathematics in India* puts it:

> The Indian development of place value decimal system ... is such a famous achievement that it would be very gratifying to have a detailed record of it. ... Exactly how and when the Indian decimal place value system first developed, and how and when a zero symbol was incorporated into it, remains mysterious.[22]

In this section, we will examine in details the evidence that is offered for India's priority-claims on zero. As explained in the previous section, history of zero cannot be understood without understanding the history of decimal place value. Our examination of the Indian case will start with decimals and decimal place values, and gradually move towards the emergence of zero. We will, as promised, juxtapose the

---

21 Charles Seife, 2000, p. 8. Emphasis added.

22 Plofker, 2009, pp. 44, 47. Even Datta and Singh, one of the earliest advocates of the exclusively Hindu origin of zero and place value admit that there are holes in the evidence: "between the finds of Mohenjodaro and the inscription of Asoka, there is a gap of 2,700 years of more," p. 20. They also acknowledge that answers to questions regarding who? Where? when? of the invention of place value are "not known," p. 49.

Indian evidence against evidence from sister Euro-Asian civilizations, and we will pay attention to everyday methods of counting and computing, in addition to Sanskrit texts.

4.1 Antiquity of the decimal system in India

It is often implied that the decimal system is an Indian invention. Often the credit for this achievement is ascribed to the inherently scientific nature of Sanskrit language. Statements like these from an eminent historian of Indian science, B.A. Subbrayappa, that "Indians' invention of the decimal system, especially zero, has paved the way for today's IT revolution", are the stuff of everyday discourse in India.[23] As we shall see, ancient Indians were in no way the first, or the only, creators of the decimal system of counting.

There is, of course, no doubt that as far back as we can go, Indians have used a decimal or a 10-based counting method. The *Ṛg Veda* and *Yajurveda* provide ample evidence that by the early Vedic times, a regularized decimal system of number counting was well established. Kim Plofker has usefully provided English translations of *shloka*s from the Vedic corpus which give a good idea of how the power of ten was used. Two representative examples are quoted below.

> You Agni, are the lord of all [offerings], you are the distributor of thousands, hundreds, tens [of good things]. *Ṛg Veda*, 2.1.8
>
> Come Indra, with twenty, thirty, forty horses; come with fifty horses yoked to your chariot, with sixty, seventy to drink the soma; Come carried by eighty, ninety and a hundred horses. *Ṛg Veda*, 2.18:5-6

By the middle-Vedic period, one finds number words for much larger powers of ten. A verse from *Yajurveda* (7.2.20) for example, offers praise to numbers which range from one, two … to *ayuta* (ten thousand), *niyuta* (hundred thousand), *prayata* (one million), *arbuda* (ten million), *nyarbuda* (hundred million), *samudra* (billion) *madhya* (ten billion), *anta* (hundred billion) *parardha* (trillion).[24]

---

23 'India invented decimal system' *The Hindu*, Feb. 17, 2007. Available at http://www. thehindu.com/todays-paper/tp-national/tp-tamilnadu/india-invented-decimal-system/article1798199.ece

24 Plofker, 2009, p. 13-16. This penchant for large numbers is a hallmark of Indian mathematical texts and we will return to this issue below.

All of this is well-established and beyond any doubt. However, counting in bundles of tens was so widely practiced, it could almost be considered universal. For example, of the 307 number systems of Native American peoples investigated in an anthropological study carried out in the early decades of the 20th century, 146 were found to be decimal and 106 of them used the base 5 or 20.[25] Moreover, as Georges Ifrah points out, counting by tens is shared by *all* members of the family of Indo-European languages. The rule in the Indo-European language-family is this: "the numbers from 1 to 9 and each of the powers of ten (100, 1000, 10,000 etc.) has a separate name, while all other numbers being expressed analytical combinations of these names."[26] Given the near universal use of decimal counting, it would have been surprising if ancient Indians had been innocent of it.

While the Indian case for ten-based numeration rests upon textual evidence, archeological evidence from Greece and China clearly shows decimal system being used for practical purposes.

The Greek evidence is found engraved on the walls of a tunnel in the island of Samos, which was constructed around 550 BCE to bring water from a spring outside the capital city. Modern archaeological excavation has revealed that the tunnel was dug by two teams who started from the opposite side and met in the middle. The numbers engraved on the walls read "10, 20, 30.... 200" from the south entrance and "10,20, 30... 300" from the north entrance, and were used to keep track of the distance dug.[27]

As far as China is concerned, Joseph Needham's judgment that "there was never a time when the Chinese did not have a decimal place value" is only partially correct.[28] The Chinese number system *as written* was based on powers of ten, but it was *not* place value. However, the Chinese *performed* their computations using counting rods, which *was*

25 Dirk Struik, 1987, p. 10.

26 Georges Ifrah, 2000, p. 31.

27 Victor Katz, pp. 34-35.

28 Needham, pp. 12-13. While the antiquity of decimal is uncontested, Needham exaggerates the antiquity of place value in Chinese numerals, which when written down, used special characters for powers of ten, hundred etc. In a true positional system, the position of the number itself will show if it is a multiple of thousand, hundred etc. without using any special characters for ten, hundred ...etc.

a decimal place value system, conceptually identical with the modern "Hindu Arabic" numerals which we use today. (We will look at the issue of place value in the next section).

The earliest evidence of Chinese number-system comes from the so-called "oracle bones" inscribed with royal records of divinations written on bones and tortoise shells dating back to 1500 BCE (See Fig-

Figure 1. Oracle bones from the Shang Dynasty in China (c. 1800-1200 BCE)

ure 1) These bones contain numerical records of tribute received, animals hunted, number of animals sacrificed, counts of days, months, and other miscellaneous quantities related to divination.[29]

The oracle bones are mathematically important because they show an advanced numeral system, which allowed any number, however large, to be expressed by the use of nine unit signs, along with a selected number of "power-signs" for representing powers of tens, twenties,

---

[29] Farmers found these bones in their fields in Henan Province at the end of the 19th century. Initially, they were thought to be "dragon" bones with medicinal value. Fortunately, they were rescued before they could be powdered and sold as medicine. Many more bones carrying similar inscriptions have been found through the last century.

hundreds, thousands etc. The standard number system used today in China is a direct descendant of the ancient Shang system.[30]

In light of this evidence, claims about the Indian invention of the decimal system must be re-evaluated.

4.2 Antiquity of decimal place value in India

As discussed above, the invention of place value is a necessary stage of mathematical development that needs to take place if an empty space in the order of numbers is to make an appearance. It is therefore understandable why Indo-centric histories lay priority claim to it finding it in Sanskrit texts written as early as 200 CE, becoming fully operational in Aryabhata's work, around 500 CE.[31]

The historical evidence is complicated by the fact that we have two distinct number systems evolving at the same time – Brahmi numerals which lack place value, and the Sanskrit number-symbols, or *bhūta-sankhyā*, which do show place-value from early centuries of the Common Era. Let us examine the evidence, starting with Brahmi numerals.

The oldest written script from the Indian subcontinent is that found on the yet un-deciphered Harrapan seals, but the oldest deciphered script is Brahmi that dates back to around 4th century BCE.

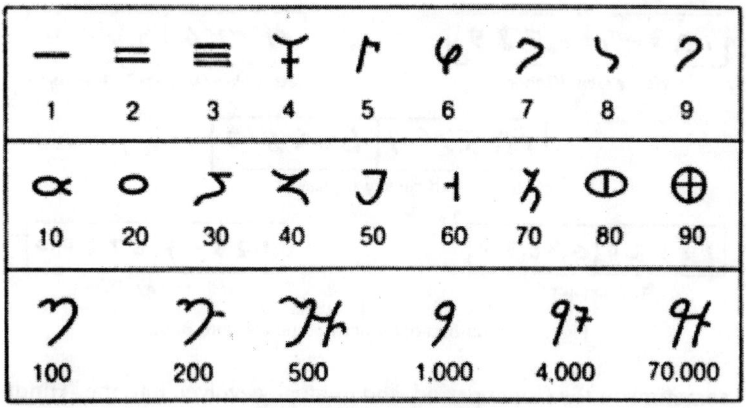

Figure 2. Brahmi Numerals

30 This description of the oracle bones is from Joseph, 2011, pp. 199-200, and Chrisomalis, 2010, pp. 260-261.

31 For a non-specialist take on this issue, see http://www.sanskritimagazine.com/vedic_science/place-value-not-zero-is-the-most-important-invention/

The general consensus is that the Brahmi script was formalized at about the time of the Mauryan emperor, Ashoka. It was devised to give written expression to the spoken language of the region, called Prakrit. The earliest inscriptions in Brahmi can be found on the rock edicts installed by Ashoka, around the middle of the third century BCE. It is in these rock edicts we get the first glimpse of how numbers were written in Brahmi. Numerals 1,4 and 6 are found in various Ashokan inscriptions, while numbers 2, 4, 6, 7 and 9 in the Nana Ghat inscriptions about a century later; and the 2, 3, 4, 5, 6, 7, and 9 in the Nasik caves of the 1st or 2nd century. Figure 2 (at page 65) is a composite of Brahmi numerals obtained from sites all over the subcontinent, including Nepal.

The familiar Nagari numerals descended from Brahmi numerals

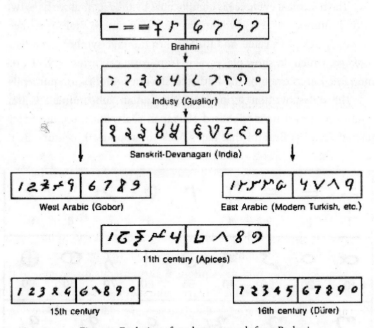

Figure 3. Evolution of modern numerals from Brahmi

sometime in the Gupta period, and gradually evolved into the "Hindu-Arabic" numerals the whole world uses today (Fig. 3).[32]

---

32 See Ifrah for an exhaustive treatment of Brahmi numerals, including speculations about their origin, pp. 367-399.

There is a consensus among historians that *Brahmi numerals did not have a concept of place value and did not have a symbol for zero*. Numerals inscribed into the wall of Nanaghat cave clearly show a number which has been deciphered as 24,400 (Fig. 4). It is written using special

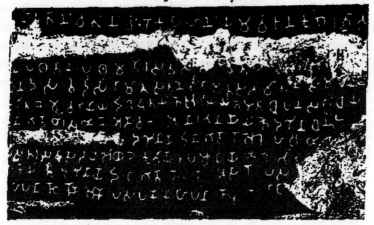

Figure 4. *A Pencil rubbing of Nanaghat Cave Inscription (second century BCE). The number 24,000 is represented by three marks occupying positions 4, 5, 6 from the left hand corner on the bottom line. Source: Hindu-Arabic Numerals, by David Eugene Smith and Louis Charles Karpinski, 1911. The Project Gutenberg EBook.*

symbols for 20,000, followed by another symbol for 4000 and 400. If these numerals had followed place-value notation it would have been written with only the numerals for 2 and 4 followed by two zeros.[33]

None of the Brahmi inscriptions with numerals discovered so far show any sign of place value.[34] Place value suddenly begins to make an appearance sometime around the sixth century, starting with the dates written on copper land-grants.[35] Gradually one begins to see numbers written without special symbols indicating power or rank; the posi-

33 See Ifrah, p. 399, for how the number 24,000 would appear in Brahmi if Brahmi were a place-value number system.

34 See Ifrah, pp. 397-398 for a compilation of various Brahmi inscriptions.

35 The authenticity of some of these copper-plates has been challenged. See Datta and Singh for details.

tion of numeral itself begins to indicate what power of ten they carried. Zero, initially a dot, begins to make an appearance around this time, the first incontrovertible proof appearing in a Gwalior temple in the year 876. (More on this in section 4.4).

There is a gap of about 900 years between Brahmi to Nagari place-value numerals. There are all kinds of wild guesses about what caused this crucial transition, but most of them are just that – guesses. Even those scholars (like Ifrah, to take a prominent example) who firmly and fervently believe that Indians alone invented zero without any outside influence, are unable to offer any clues to how this transition took place, what could have caused it, and how it spread all over the subcontinent and beyond to Southeast Asian lands.

Brahmi inscriptions disappoint us in our search for zero. However, Sanskrit scripts using *bhūta-sankhyā* (see section 3) indicate a knowledge of place value. We see this method of notation in use from Sanskrit texts starting around mid-third century CE, to around the 18th century.

The way Sanskrit number-symbols, or *bhūta-sankhyā*, were used is exemplified by the Yavana-jataka, or "Greek horoscopy", of Sphujid-havja, which is a versified form of a translated Greek work on astrology. This text places the "wise king Sphujidhavja in the year Vishnu/hook-sign/moon" which translates into numerals one (moon), nine (hook sign) and one (the deity Vishnu) giving us the year 191 of the Saka era beginning in 78 CE. (The year corresponds to 269 or 270 CE.) More mathematical examples can be cited from Surya Siddhanta, an early 6th century text, and the 14th century writings of Madhava.[36]

This manner of writing numbers shows one thing; the order in which the symbols were written or recited determined their value, with a proviso that the least significant number came first, followed by higher powers. The order itself indicated power, and there was no need to use power-words. Thus Sphujidhavja could write 191 using only three symbols.

The other textual evidence that is routinely cited to support the idea that place-value was known to Indians as early as the 5th century

---

36 For Yavana-jataka, see Plofker 2009, p. 47; for a verse from Surya Siddhanta, see Ifrah, p. 411 and for Madhava, see Pingree 2003, p. 49.

CE is a commentary on a verse of Patanjali's *Yoga Sūtras* [3.13] which reads as follows:

> Just as a line in the hundreds place means a hundred, in the tens place ten, and one in the ones place, so one and the same woman is called a mother, daughter and sister.

The author of this commentary, as Plofker rightly points out, clearly expected his audiences to be familiar with the concept of numerical symbols representing different powers of ten depending upon their position.[37]

The textual evidence is not in question. Concrete number system *is* a place value system. However cumbersome and full of ambiguities it was, there is no doubt that the order of the symbols alone determined their value.

What is in question is whether India was the first to combine decimal powers of ten with place value, as is routinely claimed. The use of concrete symbols (*bhuta*) for numbers is definitely unique to India. But was the practice of reading the value of a number from its position unique to India? Another important question has to do with the practical limitations of bhūta-sankhyā method of enumeration. Using symbols to represent numbers was a wonderful device for generating verses that rhymed and could be easily memorized, but it was most impractical for actual computations. (Try your hand at adding, subtracting, multiplying or dividing these two numbers: Vishnu-hook sign-moon and ashvin-anga-pitamaha, and you will see the problem). The following observation by Stephen Chrisomalis, author of a recent book on comparative history of numerical notations, is right on the mark:

> The bhūta-sankhyā system is suggestive of positionality, but does not constitute a system of graphic numeral signs, nor should its use be taken to imply the widespread use of decimal positional numerals in Indian manuscripts.[38]

Beyond its extensive use in recording dates and years in land-deeds, and for recording the final results of computations, *bhūta-sankhyā* system did not find much use. There is no evidence to indicate that Brahmi numerals were much in use for practical purposes either. What then,

---

37 Plofker, 2009, p. 46. Similar analogies are also recorded in the Buddhist literature, dating back to first century CE.

38 Chrisomalis, 2010, p. 195.

were the computational practices needed for commerce, account-keeping, tax-collection and myriad other uses of numbers in everyday life? We do hear of dust-boards used for computations, but we have no clue what the numerals looked like, what the rules of computation were, or who used these boards.[39]

Let us now put the development of place-value in India in a comparative perspective.

It is well-documented that as far back as 1800 BCE, the Mesopotamian cultures were using a base- 60, or sexagesimal, place-value system to write any number, however large, using just two symbols (a hook for 1 and a wedge for 10). It is also well-established that the Mayan people (of what we today call South America) had developed a base-20, or vigesimal, place-value system. But as the modern numerals have followed a base-10, or decimal system, we will exclude these outliers. That leaves us with the Greeks and the Chinese. Both civilizations had a decimal number system that used a hybrid form of place-value. What is more, both have left us evidence of well-developed technologies of practical computations – abacus in the case of Greco-Roman civilization, and counting rods in the case of China.[40]

It is well known that the Greeks thought of numbers in geometrical patterns and, consequently, remained largely preoccupied with geometry. It has been well documented elsewhere how the Greeks adapted Egyptian numbers to their own purposes, and gradually came to adopt what is called the Ionian system of numeration around sixth century BCE. This system was alphabetical: the first nine letters of the Greek alphabet were associated with numbers 1 to 9, the next nine alphabets

---

39 The best description that I have come across is from Datta and Singh: "For the calculations involved in ganita, the use of some writing material was essential. The calculations were performed on board with a chalk, or on sand (*dhuli*) spread on the ground or on a board. Thus the terms *pati-ganita* ("science of calculation on the board") or *dhuli-karma* ("dust-work") came to be used for higher mathematics. Later on, the section dealing with algebra was given the name *bija-ganita*." 1938, p. 8. They provide no further details. Robert Kaplan also refers to these sand-boards and conjectures that zero was the empty space left behind in the sand when a Greco-Roman style "counter" – most likely a rounded pebble – was moved.

40 The Chinese abacus, which is still in use, is very different from the ancient Greco-Roman abacus.

represented multiples of 10 (10, 20....90), while the last batch of alphabets (which included three archaic alphabets) stood for the first nine integral multiples of 100 (100, 200, 300...900). To take an example, 654 could be written as χνδ, where χ stands for 600, ν for 50 and δ for four. The system is not positional. Yet, as Carl Boyer pointed out, "that the Greeks had such a principle more or less in mind, is evident not only in the repeated use of symbols from α through Θ for units and thousands, but also in the fact that the symbols are arranged in order of magnitude, from the smallest on the right to the largest on the left."[41]

If we to turn to the "counter culture" of Greeks and Romans – literally, counters which could be pebbles to clay shards being moved around on counting boards – we find a positional decimal system firmly in place, with spaces left empty, signifying what we today call zero.

Archeologists have recovered actual abacuses and counting tables going as far back as the third century BCE Greece. Some thirty abacuses have so far been found in the region around the Aegean Sea, including Greece and what is now Turkey. These counting devices are simple structures, consisting of a flat surface on which lines are marked between which counters are moved. The most famous abacus is the Table of Salamis, dating back to 5th BCE (see Figures 5 and 6), and the most famous image of a money- counter using a counting board is from the Darius vase, dating back 350 BCE (see figure 7).[42]

We must include these early calculators for this reason: they operated on the principle of positional value. In other words, the pebbles/counters changed value according to the position they occupied. The basic operation was as follows:[43] counters move between lines, based upon simple equivalences between numbers. Five times ten is fifty, and therefore five counters on the ten-line are equivalent to one counter on the fifty line; likewise, two counters on the fifty line can be replaced with one counter on the one hundred-line. Suppose you have four counters on the ten-line and one counter on the fifty-line. Let us suppose you want to add ten. You add a single counter on the ten-line. Now that you

---

41 Merzbach and Boyer, 2011, p. 54.

42 See Ifrah, pp. 200-211, Kaplan, pp. 23-24.

43 From Reviel Netz, p. 326.

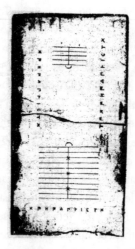

Figure 5. The Salamis Tablet, 300 BCE
Source: Ancient Computers, http://ethw.org/Ancient_Computers

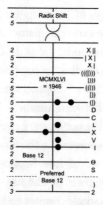

Figure 6. Roman hand abacus, mapped on to the Salamis Tablet.
Source: Ancient Computers, http://ethw.org/Ancient_Computers

Figure 7. Details of the table abacus from vase painting, "The War Council of Darius" c. 340-320 BCE. Source: Computer History Museum at http://www.computerhistory.org/

have five counters on the ten-line, you are allowed to remove all five and add one counter to the fifty-line, and so on.

Did these counters have a zero? They surely had empty spaces. As in the example above, the board was a dynamic space, constantly changing as counters moved from one line to another. But the empty space was not given a numerical sign, as most of this computation was done manually and the final number recorded in words which did not need a zero.

This procedure for counting simply assumes that the value of the same counter depends on which line it sits on. This assumption and the method of counting using the counting boards must be widespread enough for the Athenian law giver Solon (550 BCE) to have compared "a tyrant's favorite to a counter whose value depends upon the whim of the tyrant pushing it from column to column." The same words were repeated by historian Polybius (200 BCE) with some extra elaboration:

> the courtiers who surround the king are exactly like counters on the lines of a counting board. For depending upon the will of the reckoner, they may be valued either at no more than an obol, or else at a whole talent.[44]

This bears striking resemblance in logic – if not in the imagery – with the 5th century commentary on the *Yoga Sūtra* cited above. To remind ourselves: "Just as a line in the hundreds place means a hundred, in the tens place ten, and one in the ones place, so one and the same woman is called a mother, daughter and sister." The Greek sources are dated many centuries before the Indian reference. That itself proves nothing, except that Indians were neither the only ones, nor the first ones, to be familiar with the idea that a number can take on different values, depending upon the position.

But we have evidence from much closer home – China – where decimal place value was already widespread by 400 BCE. As the evidence from oracle bones shows, writing numbers in powers of tens has very ancient roots in China (just as it has in India). But a distinct use of decimal place value – where the position of a number decides its value, complete with empty space indicating absence of any numeral – was

---

44 Quoted from Kaplan, p. 22. Talent and obol are names of the Greek currency, with 30,000 obols to a talent.

already a common, everyday practice in China 400 years before the first millennium of the Common Era.

Alongside the written number ideograms (which date back to 1500 BCE oracle bones) the Chinese had their "counter-culture" rooted in practice: their "counters" were counting rods which were moved on any flat surface marked into successive powers of tens. These rods were not a mere accounting device (as the Grecian abacuses, above) but were used for all basic arithmetical operations and eventually also for solving algebraic equations. If the Chinese had transferred their rod-numerals and the mathematical operations based upon them into writing, the result would be *identical* to our modern numeration and mathematical operations like multiplication, division, root extraction etc.[45]

A very brief introduction to counting rods will be useful at this point. We will use Lam and Ang's *Fleeting Footsteps* as our guide here.

The rods were in use as far back as 400 BCE (the Warring States era). The earliest physical rods unearthed by archaeologists go back to around 170 BCE. Coins and pottery bearing rod-numeral signs have been dated to around 400 BCE. Records as far back as 202 BCE describe the first Han emperor as boasting that he alone knew "how to plan campaigns with counting rods in his tent."[46] These rods were basically short sticks about 14cm (5.5 inches) in length, made mostly of bamboo, but also of wood, bone, horn, iron or even ivory or jade (which only the very rich could afford). They were carried (all 271 of them) in a small hexagonal pouch, much like we carry electronic calculators or our smart phones today. Bags containing bundles of counting stick have been found in skeletal remains dating back to the last few centuries before the Common Era.

Who used them? Practically everybody from traders, travellers, monks to government officials, mathematicians and astronomers. In other words, whenever and wherever computation was required, the sticks came out of their bags and were spread on a mat, table top, floor

---

45 This is what Lam Lay-Yong has claimed in her work *The Fleeting Footsteps*, p. 10 and passim. The Chinese replaced the counting rods with the abacus around 12th century or so, which Yong believes set them back, as the step-by-step thinking that rod-numerals required was replaced with rote-learning.

46 Needham and Ling, p. 71.

or any flat surface. Evidence shows that during the Tang Dynasty (618-907), civil and military officials carried their bags of sticks wherever they went. The computations carried out with the sticks were written down on bamboo strips and on paper by the early centuries of the Common Era.[47] Since counting with rods was a practical skill which everyone was supposed to be familiar with, early mathematical texts (such as the 3rd century CE *Nine Chapters on the Mathematical Arts*, and *The Mathematical Classic of Zhou Gnomon* that we referred to in the last chapter) don't elaborate on how to use them. But a 4th century book attributed to a Master(Zi) Sun titled *Sun zi Suanjing* (the *Mathematical Classic of Master Sun*), provides details of how computation was to be carried out with rods. This book was later included in the set of ten mathematical classics put together during the Tang Dynasty that all aspiring state officials had to study in order to pass the entrance exams. In the early centuries of the Common Era, rod numeral computations spread to Japan, Korea, Vietnam and other areas in the South-East influenced by both India and China.

How were the rods used? The method is simple and ingenuous.

The first nine numerals were formed using the rods in the following two arrangements: one in which the rods are vertical (*zong*) and the other in which the rods are horizontal (*heng*)

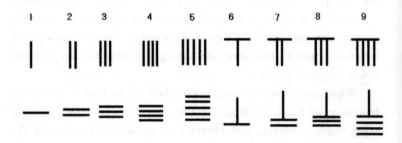

Figure 8: Counting rods placed vertically, *zong*, top row; Rods arranged horizontally, *heng*, bottom row.

---

47 Paper was invented by the Chinese around 100 CE, though some archaeological findings put the date further back by a century or two.

To write numbers greater than 10, the rods were set up in columns. The right-most column was for units, the next one for tens, the next for hundreds, and so on. A blank column meant no rods were to be placed there, meaning what we mean today when we write a zero. The Chinese called the empty space in rod-numerals as *kong*, 空, which means empty, just as Hindus called an empty space *śunya*. (More on zero in Chinese numerals in 4.4). To make it easier to read the columns, zongs and hengs were alternated: vertical arrangement of rods (*zong*) was used in the unit column, the hundreds column and ten thousand column and so on, while the horizontal (*heng*) arrangement was used in tens, thousand, hundred thousand.[48] Here are some illustrative examples:[49]

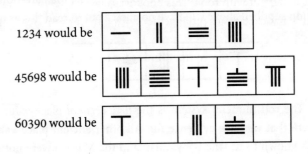

The columns could be extended in *both directions,* with columns to the right of the units column containing negative numbers which were represented by rods of a different color. The rods were used for addition, subtraction, multiplication and division, the rules for which are laid out in Sun Zi's book, translated and explained in *Fleeting Footsteps*. In fact, in her lecture when she was awarded the Kenneth May medal for her distinguished career, Lam Lay Yong took the audience step-by-step through the steps for multiplication and division that the great 9th century Muslim mathematician and astronomer al-Khwarizmi uses, to

---

48 The following formula from Sun zi sums up the arrangement: "the units are vertical and the tens horizontal, the hundreds stand and the thousands prostrate, thousands and tens look alike, and so do ten thousand and hundreds." Lam and Ang, p. 47.

49 All examples are from MacTutor website. http://www-history.mcs.st-and.ac.uk/HistTopics/Chinese_numerals.html

show that his method is *identical* to the method that Sun Zi lays out in his classic text. [50]

What interests us are the following similarities between the Chinese rod-numerals and the modern "Hindu-Arabic" numerals. (They could not be more different in how they look, but looks are deceptive):

There is an exact correspondence between rod numerals and the Hindu-Arabic (i.e. modern) decimal place values numerals – to use Lam's words "the two are conceptually identical".[51] In both systems, only nine numbers and a sign for an empty space are all that is needed to write any number, however large or small. In both systems, the numerical values of the digits are built into their positions, going in ascending power of ten from right to left. Anyone with just the bare-bones information supplied above will have no choice but to read this as 60390.

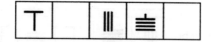

The rod-numeral system is the first *decimal* place-value number system that we have evidence for. All other ancient place-value notations known to us (the Babylonian and the Mayan) were not decimal. Even though Brahmi was decimal, we have already established that Brahmi numerals, which are almost the exact contemporaries of rod numerals, did not use place value. For this reason, Lam points out, correctly it seems, that "Brahmi could not have been the *conceptual* precursor of Hindu Arabic system", while fully accepting that *the shape* of Hindu-Arabic numerals did evolve from Brahmi via Devanagari.[52] (We will return to the rod-numerals in section 4.4).

---

50 According to the *Encyclopaedia Britannica*, Muḥammad ibn Mūsā al-Khwārizmī (born *c*. 780 – died *c*. 850), was a Muslim mathematician and astronomer whose major works introduced Hindu-Arabic numerals and the concepts of algebra into European mathematics. Latinized versions of his name and of his most famous book title live on in the terms *algorithm* and *algebra*.

51 Lam, pp. 172, 173.

52 Lam, p. 177.

4.3 Antiquity of large numbers in India

The Hindus, the Buddhists and the Jains are well known for using extravagantly large numbers in their cosmological speculations. A verse from the *Yajurveda* that offers prayers to numbers that go up to a trillion has been cited above (section 4.1). The Buddhist text, *Lalitavistara* which was written around 300 CE tells the story of Buddha who has been challenged to recite the names of all powers of ten beyond a *koti* (i.e., 10 million), each rank being a hundred times greater than the previous one. The Buddha successfully recites all the names, going up to the 421st power of ten – that is, one followed by 421 zeros. Many other examples of breathtakingly large numbers have been documented.[53]

No one has been able to explain this strange penchant for immense numbers. These numbers were obviously not obtained by any kind of physical measurements, nor did they refer to what exactly was being counted. Such flights of imagination were obviously of no use in everyday mathematics. As Sal Restivo points out:

> [immense cosmological numbers of the Hindus]... are means for transcending experience, used for the purpose of *mystification*, or to convey the notion that some thing or being is *impressive*, they are symbols in a mathematical rhetoric designed to awe the listener into a religious posture... The social roots of this distinctive mathematical system lie in the particularly exalted status of Indian religious specialists.[54]

We could have let the matters rest there. However, many notable historians see the Indic penchant for large numbers not as a source of mystification, but as a source of mathematical genius, which led to the origin of place value and the invention of zero. Ifrah summarizes this position thus:

> The early passion which Indian civilization had for high numbers was a significant factor contributing to the discovery of the place-value system, and not only offered the Indians the incentive to go beyond the "calculable" physical world, but also led to an understanding (much earlier than in our [western] civilization) of the notion of mathematical infinity itself.[55]

In other words, creativity in mathematics is ascribed largely (if not solely) to experience-transcending speculations. The actual math-

---

53 Kaplan, pp. 37-40; Ifrah, pp. 421-426.
54 Restivo, 1992, p. 49. Emphasis in the original.
55 Ifrah, p. 421.

ematical practices of the calculable world around us are not taken into consideration.

But what *is* the connection between these enormous numbers and discovery of place value and eventually zero? How are the two related?

For some the connection is obvious and needs no further evidence or elaboration. Example of this faith-based history comes from the well-known *History of Hindu Mathematics* in which the authors, Datta and Singh, repeatedly inform the reader that "While the Greeks had no terminology for denominations above the myriad (10^4), and the Romans above the mille (10^3), the ancient Hindus dealt freely with no less than eighteen denominations. ... The numeral language of no other nation is as scientific and perfect as that of the Hindus." From this they simply surmise that "even at a remote period, the Hindus must have possessed a well-developed system of numerical symbols", and again that all these large numbers "would have been impossible unless arithmetic had attained a considerable degree of progress..."[56]

More recently, in his well-known work *Crest of the Peacock*, George Gheverghese Joseph has made a similar argument. After citing large numbers from *Yajurveda* and *Ramayana,* and comparing India favorably against Greeks for stopping at a woefully small 10^4, he points out what is obviously true: that "the Vedic Indians were quite at home with very large numbers". However, he goes on to conclude, like Datta and Singh, that this *must have* led to the development of place value:

> The early use of such large numbers eventually led to the adoption of a series of names for the successive powers of ten. The importance of these number-names in the evolution of decimal place value notation cannot be exaggerated. The word-numeral system, later replaced by alphabetic notation, was the logical outcome of proceeding by the multiples of ten....[57]

This argument fails to convince. For one, decimal system – that is, counting by power of tens – does not itself imply place value. As explained earlier, counting by the powers of tens can happily carry on without inventing a system in which the same number acquires a different value depending upon where it is placed. Yes, there are verses where

---

56   Datta and Singh, 1939, pp. 9, 20, 36. They believe that the existence of large numbers also "proves" that "Hindus invented the Brahmi number system" (p. 36).

57   Joseph, 2011, pp. 340-341.

number-symbols (*bhutas*) are used alone and their value is understood by the sequence in which they are uttered (see section 2). *But* bhūta-sankhyā *was used only in the verse portions of mathematical texts.* The prose commentaries that accompanied these verses used number words to express large numbers which did not need a place value system of notation. Thus what we will today write as 3045 would be expressed as *tri* (three) *sahastra* (thousand), and *chatvaarimshat* (four times ten), *pancha* (five), where *sahastra* and *chatvaarimshat* are power-words.[58]

The second flaw in this argument has to do with factually incorrect historical details. If we place Indian evidence in a comparative perspective, we can clearly see that it was neither the first nor the only civilization that was comfortable with large numbers. We will again bring in the Greeks and the Chinese.

To begin with, it is simply incorrect that the Greeks could not handle numbers larger than 10,000. Even a cursory familiarity with Greek numerals would show that they could write any number, however large, using their alphabetical numerals. It is true that they did not have special names (or alphabets) for numbers larger than a myriad (10,000) which they represented with the Greek letter M (pronounced *mu*). But that is hardly the end of the story: a myriad was simply the beginning of a new count which they represented by writing the number of myriads above M. For example, the number 71,750, 000 was written as αM‚ζροε; 2,056,839,184 becomes βMκ΄, αM‚εχ π γ, ‚θρ π δ and so on.[59]

Those who continue to glibly put our ancestors ahead of all others must pay attention to the well known work by Archimedes (287-212 BCE) called the *Sand Reckoner* in which the great Greek mathematician and engineer teaches Gelon, the king of Syracuse, how to find out how many grains of sand there are in the universe. He provides names for increasingly larger orders of a myriad-myriad (that is 10^8) all the way to 10 to the power of 80,000 million million! Archimedes accomplishes

---

58 See Filliozat, 2004 for more on the distinction between how numbers are expressed in verse and commentary.

59 The example of large numbers and their Greek notations are from Katz, p. 34 and from the Greek Number Convertor available at http://www.russellcottrell.com/greek/utilities/greeknumberconverter.htm. For more details, consult Boyer, 1944.

this task without the use of a zero, as he uses number-words for the various orders of 10^8.[60]

As Robert Kaplan has pointed out, there are striking similarities between Archimedes' method and the story about Buddha that is told in *Lalitavistara* described at the beginning of this section. According to Kaplan, there are structural similarities between the two accounts, including even the mention of poppy seeds. Kaplan admits that "clues are thin on the ground", but he posits the possibility of Greek influence on the evolution of Indian numerals, including the sign of zero which he believed came from the empty place left behind on Indian sand-boards when Greek-style pebble-counting spread into India.[61] If the clues are as thin as Kaplan believes them to be, it is better to withhold judgement and simply admit that question of transmission is perhaps un-answerable at this stage.

Turning now to China, we find that the humble counting rods were capable of not just expressing any number, however large. They were capable of carrying out basic arithmetical manipulations with large numbers as well. The following example excerpted here from Lam's work will suffice:

> In *Sun Zi suanjing* is found the following: Multiply 708,588 by 531, 441 to obtain 376,572,715, 308. When this is divided among 354,294 persons, each person gets 1,062, 882.[62]

Sun Zi suanjing, remember, is a 4th century text that describes the rules and methods of carrying out mathematical operations using counting-rods. It goes without saying that the above problem was solved using counting rods.

Once again, India cannot rightfully claim to be ahead of other civilizations of comparable age and development when it comes to comfort with very large numbers. What is most important to note is that the comparative perspective shows that facility with naming large numbers is neither necessary nor sufficient for the development of decimal place value and zero. If that were the case, Greek mathematicians, especially Archimedes, would also have hit upon the idea. On the other hand, we

60   Kaplan, 1999, chapter 3.
61   Kaplan, 1999, chapter 4.
62   Lam and Ang, 2004, p. 14.

have seen that both Greek and Chinese "counter-cultures" – hands-on, everyday calculations – were literally born with decimal place-value, without which there was no need to represent an empty space in a non-metaphysical, computational sense. So perhaps, zero was born in the streets, far away from the ashrams, academies, or mandarin schools where learned philosophers thought deep thoughts about the void or nothingness.

4.4. The emergence of zero
The following facts are well-established about the emergence of zero in the sub-continent and its cultural sphere in South-East Asia:

- *Śunya-bindu* as a numeral represented initially by a dot begins to differentiate from the metaphysical concept of *śunya* as void or nothingness sometime around 600 CE – which is also the time when Brahmi-derived, non-place value numerals begin to give way to place value numerals.[63]
- The earliest surviving and unquestioned evidence of *śunya-bindu* as a numeral comes *not* from India, but from Cambodia. It comes from an inscription from a stone pillar which in part says "the Chaka era reached year 605 on the fifth day of the waning moon." The '0' in 605 is represented by a dot. As we know that the Chaka era began in the year 78 A.D., the date of this zero is 683, nearly two centuries *before* the first zero shows up in India. (See plate 1)

  The Cambodian inscription was documented first by a French scholar George Codes in 1931. The site where the pillar stood was plundered by the Khmer Rouge and no one knew what became of it. It was re-discovered – in a storage shed near the great temple of Angkor Wat – in 2013 by Amir Aczel, an American-Israeli mathematician and a historian of science.[64]

  The Cambodian zero is not a fluke. Similar inscriptions

---

63 According to Chrisomalis (2010, p. 196) *śunya-bindu* was first used in Subhandu's poetical work, *Vasavadatta*, written around the 6th century.

64 Aczel has written about this discovery in many forums (apart from a book). See 'How I rediscovered the oldest zero in history', available at The Crux, an online

with a dot for a zero are found in Sumatra and Banka islands of Indonesia, dated 683 and 686 CE respectively. There are many more inscriptions, too numerous to list here, from other South-East Asian lands, especially the present day Malaysia and Indonesia.[65] The implications of the fact that zero shows up first in South-East Asia before it makes its appearance in India have not been fully absorbed by Indian historians, as we will see in the next section.

- The first rock engravings in India that indicate the use of zero in numbers that use decimal place value date back to the second half of the 9th century. The most well known is the inscription from the Chaturbhuja temple, a rock temple dedicated to Vishnu, near the city of Gwalior. (see plate 2) Inside the temple (which is no longer used for worship), next to the *murti* of the deity, there is an inscription dated year 933 in the Vikram calendar (which translates into 876 CE). The inscription is about a gift of land, measuring 270 x187 hastas, to the temple. This land was to be turned into a flower garden, from which 50 garlands were to be offered to the deity everyday. What makes this inscription a milestone in the history of mathematics is that the numbers 933, 270, and 50 are written in Nagari numerals using place-value and a small empty circle representing zero. This is the first undisputed evidence of the use of zero in a number found in India. (see plate 3)

- Two other pieces of *contested* evidence are still cited as evidence for Indian priority over decimal place value numerals with zero. The first piece of evidence is a set of copper plates bearing inscriptions about land-grants dating from 594 to 972 CE, and they are sometimes offered as evidence that zero and place value were known to us much before the Gwalior inscription. However, the authenticity of the plates has been questioned.[66]

The other piece of evidence is the famous Bakshali manu-

---

magazine. See also his narrative of the discovery 'The Origin of the Number', at the website of the Smithsonian.

65　See Needham and Ling, 1959, p. 11. An exhaustive list is provided by Ifrah.

66　See Ifrah, pp. 400-402, Datta and Singh, 1938.

script found in 1881 in the village called Bakshali in the north-western region in modern-day Peshawar, Pakistan. The part-ly-rotted birch-bark manuscript contains problems involving basic arithmetic, and clearly uses a dot in place-value numer-als. Augustus F. R. Hoernle, the Indian-born Indologist of Ger-man descent who first studied the text, dated the work to the 3rd or the 4th century CE. But that date has been questioned by later historians, notably by Takao Hayashi in 1995 who places the mathematics contained in the text to be as late as 7th cen-tury. If Hayashi is right – as claimed by a general consensus among scholars – then the earlier date for zero in decimal place value is ruled out.[67]

- Once the Classical or Siddhantic period of astronomy and mathematics begins, the rest of the story has a clear narra-tive which has the feel of an oft-told-tale. Aryabhata, whose famous work, *Aryabhatiya*, was written in 510 CE, created his own (rather cumbersome) alphabetic numeral system which nobody followed after he died. Ifrah succinctly describes what happened after Aryabhata:

Varhamihira (c. 575) who in his major work *Panchasiddhantika*, men-tioned the use of zero in mathematical operations, as did Bhaskara in 629 in his commentary on *Aryabhatiya*. In 628 in *Brahmaguptasiddhanta*, Brahmagupta defined zero as the result of subtraction between of a num-ber by itself (a- a=0) and described its properties in the following terms: 'when zero is added to a number or subtracted from a number, the num-ber remains unchanged, and a number multiplied by zero becomes zero.' .... [And thus] modern algebra was born and the mathematician had thus formulated the basic rules... this brilliant civilization opened the way to... development of mathematics and exact sciences.[68]

---

67 And yet one finds a scholar of the caliber of Joseph who seems unable to let go of the earlier date for this manuscript. After repeatedly endorsing Hayashi, Joseph continues to use Bakshali as "substantial piece of evidence, after Jaina mathemat-ics, to bridge the long gap between the *Śulvasūtra*s of the Vedic period and the mathematics of the classical period which began around 500 CE." p. 358. Clearly, if the manuscript is dated after 7th century, this statement is incorrect.

68 Ifrah, p. 439. Ifrah has an entire chapter titled 'Dictionary of the Numerical Sym-bolism of Indian Civilization' where he expands upon these ideas. The interested reader is advised to consult this dictionary.

After all this, the standard story-line is simple: India's generous gift spread to all corners of the world. Arab mathematicians picked up numerals from India and transmitted them to Europe. Buddhist monks from India took the Hindu numerals, complete with place-value and the symbol for zero, with them to China. Because the decimal numerals with a zero were so much more convenient than any other numeral system for actually manipulating numbers, the entire world discarded their old numbers and adopted the Hindu-Arabic numerals. Thanks to us, the world learned how to count.

We must now do what we have done throughout this chapter; we must look at the Indian evidence in a comparative perspective.

Even though there were possibilities inherent in the Greco-Roman abacuses, place-value and zero did not take root in that culture. But what happened in China is a different matter entirely. In China place-value and blank spaces on counting-boards indicating that a particular rank (unit, hundred, thousand…) had no number had become a part of commonsense What is interesting is that in China the walls that separated the "specialists" and the "street" were breached to some extent; the same method was being used by high and low, by the Mandarins and the learned monks as well as the illiterate farmer or the trader. Because the "learned" were not separated by high walls of status (at least in this practical technique), the method of counting sticks became codified in texts like those of Sun Zi's and became a part of the scientific tradition.

The Chinese had a name for the empty spaces on their counting boards: they called them "kong", 空, which is exactly how Indians used the word "śunya". Later on, the exact date is not known, the notation for "ling" (玲) meaning "last small raindrops after a storm" was used to represent a zero.[69] So without a doubt, "a strictly decimal positional system" with a "kong" for an empty space first appears in China, at least four centuries before the Common Era. [70]

---

69 Needham and Ling, p. 16.
70 Quoted from Ifrah, p. 279.

5. The Chinese origin of zero: Lam-Needham thesis

We come back to the question we started out with: Is it *really* established beyond reasonable doubt that ancient India was the original source of the number zero and the decimal numbering system that is the foundation of modern mathematics?

The answer can only be in the negative.

In light of the fact that a decimal place-value, conceptually identical with modern Hindu-Arabic numerals, was fully functional in China around the time when non-place value Brahmi numerals were barely emerging in India, some skepticism – and some humility – is warranted. This means that we must pay serious attention to the lines of possible transmission from China, through South-East Asia to the Indian sub-continent, that Needham and his Chinese colleagues hypothesized in 1959, and that Lam has argued for more recently.

So far, Indian historians have simply assumed a one-way transmission of mathematical ideas from India to China. But if we look closely, the transmission was always two-way, with at least as much coming from China into India as the other way around. Moreover, if we look past the monks carrying Buddhist wisdom to also include Indian merchants hazarding the mountain passes through Tibet and sailing through the Bay of Bengal, past South East Asian islands to reach China, it becomes entirely plausible that they could have brought the Chinese way of counting with them. The beauty of this conjecture is that it can solve two puzzles in the biography of zero:

1. The first puzzle is the gap of nearly 900 years between Brahmi non-place decimals, to Nagari place value decimals numerals complete with a *śunya-bindu*. (see section 4.2).

2. The other puzzle has to do with why zero appears in Cambodia and Indonesian islands before it shows up in Gwalior? (see section 4.4).

It is customary to date Indo-Chinese contact when China established an embassy in the court of the Guptas.[71] But that is not entirely true. We know from the account left behind by Zhan Qian, who first

---

71 Joseph, p. 304.

explored the lands beyond the Western frontier of China in 138 BCE, that bamboo and cotton from southwestern provinces of China that were being supplied by Indian caravans were being sold as far west as Bactria, the land that straddles today's Afghanistan, Pakistan and Ta-jikistan. China was familiar enough to find a reference in the *Mahabharata*. Moreover, Indians were not the only travellers: Pre-Islamic Arabs, Greeks, Persians and Central Asians have been travelling the many "silk routes" since 130 BCE, when the Chinese opened their western border.[72]

Likewise, it is not at all clear that South East Asian countries were purely Hindu kingdoms, as is often argued to explain away the puzzle that zero appears in Cambodia and Indonesian islands before it appears in Gwalior. The fact is that even those parts of South-East Asia that were under the cultural and political influence of Hinduism – including Cambodia, parts of Vietnam, Thailand, Laos and Burma – were in constant contact with China. To quote Prabodh C. Bagchi, the author of a book on India-China relations:

> For over a thousand years, the entire Indo-Chinese peninsula and the islands of the Indian archipelago were for all practical purposes a Greater India. Indian colonizers had set up flourishing kingdoms. Indian culture permeated the people of the country. Regular lines of communication by sea connected these kingdoms with India on the one hand, and with China on the other.[73]

This bi-cultural nature of Southeast Asia lies at the heart of Needham's conjecture cited earlier (section 2) that the symbol for zero is "an Indian garland thrown around the nothingness of the vacant space on the Han counting boards". How Needham elaborates this conjecture deserves to be reproduced in full:

> We are free to consider the possibility (or even the probability) that the written zero symbol, the more reliable calculations it permitted really originated in *the eastern zone of Hindu culture where it met the southern zone of the culture of the Chinese.* What ideographic stimulus it could have received at that interface? Could it have adopted an encircled vacancy from the empty blanks left for zeros on the Chinese counting boards? The essential point is that the Chinese had possessed, long before the time of time of Sun Tzu Suan Ching (late +3rd century) a fundamentally decimal place-value system. It may be then that the 'empti-

---

72 Bagchi, p. 7.
73 Bagchi, p. 25.

ness' of Taoist mysticism, no less than the "void" of Indian philosophy, contributed to the invention of symbol for śunya, the zero. *It would seem, indeed, that the findings of the first appearance of zero in dated inscriptions on the borderline of the Indian and the Chinese culture-areas can hardly be a coincidence.*[74]

This thesis, as we have seen, has received a second wind from the writings of Lam Lay Yong. Lam endorses Needham's conjecture, and strongly argues for the Chinese origin of zero, but her evidence comes more from the conceptual identity between the Chinese and the "Hindu-Arabic" mathematical procedures described in three Arabic texts.[75] Lam's work opens a fresh line of inquiry, namely, the Arab-Chinese cultural exchanges which go back to pre-Islamic era and were intensified after the birth of Islam. (As Prophet Mohammad advised his followers, "seek knowledge as far as China"). The direct contact between Chinese and Islamic mathematicians and scientists is too complicated to be discussed here.

Contemporary historians are split over the relevance of the Chinese evidence for understanding the evolution of Indian mathematical ideas. Some like Ifrah and Chrisomalis dismiss the very idea of zero as anything but purely Indian, while others like Joseph and Plofker advise against such summary dismissal. More balanced is the opinion of Victor Katz, author of a well-respected textbook on the history of mathematics, who looks on the invention of zero as a multi-step process by which India and China built upon each other's ideas. Katz's words deserve to be quoted at length, because they happen to exactly coincide with the surmise of this essay:

> It has been suggested that the true origins of the system in India come from the Chinese counting boards. The counting board was a portable object. Certainly Chinese traders [and Buddhist seekers as well] who visited India carried these along. In fact, since Southeast Asia is the border between Hindu culture and Chinese influence, it may have well been in that area where the interchange took place. What may have happened is that the Indians were impressed with the idea of using only nine symbols. But they naturally took for their symbols the ones they had already been using. They then improved upon the Chinese

---

74 Needham and Wang, pp. 11-12, emphasis added. The quote about the "garland" appears on p. 148.

75 These texts are: "a Latin translation of al-Khwarizmi's work on arithmetic, al-Uqlidisi's *Kitab al-Fusul fi al-Hisab al-Hindi*, and Kushyar ibn Labban's *Kitab fi usual Hisab al-Hind*". Lam, p. 178.

system for counting rods, for using exactly the same symbols for each place value, rather than alternating two types of symbols [horizontal and vertical]. And because they needed to be able to write numbers in some form, rather than just have them on the counting board, they were forced to use a symbol, the dot and later the circle to represent the blank column of the counting board. If this theory is correct, it is somewhat ironic that the Indian scientists then returned the favor and brought the new system back to China in the 8th century.[76]

If Katz is right – as he seems to be, in light of the material we have discussed at length in these pages – then it should help explain one more puzzle: why are there no written records in India which mention Chinese way of computation, while there are plenty of translated "Brahmin" texts in astronomy in China? The answer seems to be that the counting rods and the methods of using them were not written in books, but learnt through practice. It will be futile to look for evidence in learned texts. The evidence lies in the counter-culture of traders, travellers and even monks who, to use Needham's words, "had exchanged metaphysics for mathematics".

6. Concluding remarks

This chapter has tried to present the history of zero in a new key. A comparative, practice-centered perspective is what sets this account apart from the traditional histories of zero that dominate the historical scholarship, and saturate the public sphere, in India.

I hope that the evidence provided in this chapter will encourage the readers to look beyond national or civilizational boundaries to develop a deeper understanding of how ideas evolve through a give-and-take between civilizations, and how civilizations build upon ideas and practices that travel back-and-forth across trade routes, pilgrimage circuits and political relations.

I hope, moreover, that this chapter succeeds in planting in the readers' minds a seed of doubt about "purity" of ideas. There is nothing "pure" about "pure mathematics," for there is a constant interplay between practices and concepts. Neither is there anything in history of science that is "purely" Indian, or "purely" European, Chinese, or

---

76 Katz, p. 235.

Islamic. History of science is a wonderful example of history of inter-civilizational exchange of ideas. Confining it within nationalistic frameworks can only lead to a tunnel vision, and there is no reason why we should accept such a limitations on our ability to see the wider vistas that encompass the whole world.

CHAPTER 3

Genetics, Plastic Surgery and Other Wonders of Ancient Indian Medicine

1. Introduction

As the title suggests, this chapter is about medical knowledge in ancient India. But it is more than that. It also proposes a plan for combating pseudohistory of science – a plan that has the potential to turn the mania for mythic history into an opportunity for learning.

Even a cursory look at news headlines will show that we are inundated these days with myths of our civilization's singular greatness. A narrative of Indic, or *dharmic,* exceptionalism is under construction which celebrates its spiritual and scientific riches. Not unlike American exceptionalism, Indic exceptionalism seeks to universalize itself, both at home and around the world.[1]

The myth of Indic exceptionalism is a myth wrapped in and around myths taken straight out of the *Mahabharata,* the *Ramayana* and the many *Puranas,* the traditional storehouses of mythology. The

---

1   *Dharmic* civilization is understood as the civilization that is native to the land of India. It subsumes Hinduism, Buddhism, Jainism and Sikhism. Its distinctive set of assumptions regarding "divinity, the cosmos and humanity" are seen as offering "an Indian challenge to Western Universalism," as the subtitle of a recent book by Rajiv Malhotra (2011) would have it. The point to note is that the Indic/dharmic tradition by definition excludes those Indian religious traditions with roots in the Judeo-Christian and Islamic traditions.

new myth-makers appropriate popular myths from this rich tradition, evacuate religious or spiritual meanings out of them, and retell them *as if* they are literally true accounts of scientific and technological achievements. The much beloved gods and goddesses that are imprinted in the collective psyche of Indian people remain – but now they serve the earthly ambitions of men and women.

A myth, according to the Oxford English Dictionary, is "a traditional story, especially one concerning the early history of a people or explaining a natural or social phenomenon, and typically involving supernatural beings or events: *ancient Celtic myths." Myth also means, according to OED again,* "A widely held but false belief or idea."

Both meanings of myth are at work in the public sphere in India today, with one important difference: rather than see myths for what they are – "traditional stories.....involving supernatural beings," or as "widely held false beliefs" – they are being served up as legitimate evidence of scientific achievements. Like fundamentalists everywhere who insist upon reading religious texts as literal accounts of the creation and evolution of the universe, in India too, the miraculous prowess of supernatural beings is being interpreted as if they provide a literally true account of the achievements of ancient "scientists" and "engineers."

This chapter will offer a creative way we can turn this fiasco into a teaching moment. The basic idea is simple: whenever our political leaders dish out myths and call them "science," we should take it upon ourselves to learn some *real* history of *real* science in the specific domain in question.[2] After we are done laughing at the absurdity of the tall-tales we are told, we should get down to the more sober task of educating ourselves with the actual history of science in India as a part of the global history of medicine, science and technology. This self-education requires that we arm ourselves with the best, the most reliable evidence available and approach it with a critical, or a scientific, spirit – that is, *be willing to rethink our preconceived ideas in the light of compelling evidence.*[3] This is what this chapter intends to do for history of medicine

---

2   I think of it as my "lemonade model," inspired by the old proverb, "when world gives you lemons, make lemonade."

3   Here Garrett Fagan, a critic of pseudo-archeology, is right on the mark: "a basic characteristic of genuine [as opposed to pseudo-] archeology, of whatever theoret-

(as the previous two chapters have tried to do for two landmarks in mathematics)

Such an exercise, carried out with rigor, honesty and a sturdy respect for historical evidence can yield rich dividends. Its usefulness for countering ideologically-driven pseudohistory of science is obvious. Less obvious, but perhaps more important, is how a dose of *real* history can save the ancient physicians, craftsmen-mathematicians from becoming civilizational icons (as in the Indocentric discourse), or from becoming totally invisible (as in the Eurocentric discourse). Understanding how the ancients grappled with the natural world armed with nothing more than their faculty to reason and the evidence of their senses, can save them from both glorification and condescension at the hands of their 21st century inheritors.

2. Mythologizing medicine

Scholarly study of myths has come a long way from the 19th century understanding of myths as proto-scientific explanations of nature. Throughout the 20th century, as scientific understanding of the natural world made progress, " the physical world was conceded to [modern] science," as Robert Segal, a leading theorist of myth put it, and myths were no longer seen as competing with science as explanations of nature; they were instead reconceived as symbolic narratives about the place of human beings in the world, their unconscious fears and fantasies, their sense of right or wrong.[4] As Sudhir Kakar, the pre-eminent interpreter of the "inner world" of Indians puts it, "myths... are individual psychology projected onto the outside world... myths can be read as a kind of collective historical conscience, instructions from the venerable ancestors on 'right' or 'wrong,' which serves to bind the members of a group to each other."[5]

---

ical bent, is the maintenance of conceptual flexibility – a willingness to re-examine favored conclusions in the face of... countervailing evidence, and to change those conclusions accordingly. *It is not unreasonable to brand such an intellectual stance as broadly "scientific" insofar as it accepts the capacity of the data to reshape interpretations"* (emphasis added), Fagan, 2006, p.25

4   Robert Segal, 2006, pp. 341-342.

5   Sudhir Kakar, 1981, p. 4.

In India of the 21st century we seem to be stuck in the 19th century: Myths continue to crop up in history of science *as if* they are literally true accounts of the physical world, or as literally true descriptions of technological artifacts. Existence of ancient Vedic-era space-ships capable of inter-galactic travel, the existence of nuclear weapons in the time of the *Mahabharata* and other such fantastic tales continue to be asserted by learned men and women in academic forums.

It is in this context that when the Prime Minister of India used mythology as evidence for the existence of advanced knowledge of genetics and surgery in ancient India, it made news not just in India, but around the world. One could not but read Mr. Modi's words as giving official blessings to the mythification of science that has been going on in the country for a long time, but which seems to intensified under his watch.

Speaking at the inauguration ceremony Sir H.N. Reliance Foundation Hospital and Research Center in Mumbai on October 25, 2014, Modi invoked familiar Hindu myths to exhort the audience to take pride in the medical achievements of our ancestors. The Hindi text of his speech is available on the official website of the Prime Minister's Office. Excerpts in English translation are reproduced here.

Karna in the *Mahabharata,* Modi suggested, could well have been a medical first; a baby born *in-vitro.* This is what he said: "We can feel proud of what our country achieved in medical science at one point of time. We all read about Karna in the *Mahabharata.* If we think a little more, we realize that the *Mahabharata* says Karna was not born from his mother's womb. This means that genetic science was present at that time. That is why Karna could be born outside his mother's womb."

Next, Modi invoked Lord Ganesh in the context of plastic surgery. "We worship Lord Ganesh. There must have been some plastic surgeon at that time who got an elephant's head on the body of a human being, and began the practice of plastic surgery."

The PM stopped at Ganesh. But following this line of thinking, many more medical firsts can be claimed. After all, we worship Hanuman, and so there must have been biophysicist who could make this member of higher primates fly. We worship gods and goddesses with any number of fully-functional arms and heads and so there must have been neurosurgeons way back then. So on and so forth.   T h e point is that if we are not going to respect any boundary between myth and science, then history of science simply collapses into mythology. Myths interpreted literally come to serve not just as evidence for rudimentary or proto-science, but for the most cutting-edge sciences that we have *today*.

No doubt this bit of myth-making at the hospital was done with best intentions of encouraging pursuit of science. As Modi explained, "What I mean to say is that we are the country which had these capabilities. We need to regain these."

One could well complain that we are making too much of these remarks. After all, don't all politicians, from the Left and the Right, go into a grandstanding mode time to time? This is what politicians do.

But Modi, as is well-known, is a product of the *shakha* culture of the RSS. Having joined the local *shakha* when he was barely eight-years old, the RSS "[has done] the most to shape him and his worldview, and to advance his political ambitions," to quote from Vinod Jose's biographical essay on the rise of Narendra Modi.[6] Fables about "scientific" achievements of our Hindu forefathers are as natural in the RSS culture as water is for fish. With the RSS in an unprecedented position of power, there is every reason to fear that this mythology will find a place in textbooks. This is one very good reason why we must take the PM's pronouncements seriously.[7]

---

6   Vinod Jose, The *Caravan*, March 2012.

7   All signs are pointing to a massive push for the Saffronization of education. Earlier this year, the Ministry of Human Resource Development began its consultative process for a New Education Policy. It has invited input from grassroots movements regarding 33 topics related to school and higher education posted on its website http://mhrd.gov.in/. The RSS is a major player in the consultative process. According to the *Deccan Herald*, "Amid these initiatives and plans of the government, the Rashtriya Swayamsevak Sangh's (RSS) education wing is silently working to assist the government formulate the new policy. A Shiksha Niti Aayog (education policy commission), set up under the leadership of controversial educationist and former RSS pracharak Dinanath Batra, is holding parallel, nationwide deliberations to get suggestions from the "right-minded" citizens of the country. It has plans to hold at least 500 seminars across the country to "make people aware of the drawbacks of the current education system and get vital

This mythic history of medicine has implications for health policy as well. Under the Modi government, AYUSH, the government body that oversees traditional medical systems, has been elevated to a full-fledged ministry with an annual budget of 1,200 crore rupees. Even though the number of randomized control trials for Ayurveda can be counted on the "fingers of one hand," and even though homeopathy has been proven multiple times to be utterly ineffective in rigorous double-blind trials, resources are going to be diverted to these medical traditions which are more aptly described as alternatives *to* medicine, rather than as alternative medicine.[8]

The situation is ripe to put "the plan" into action, that is, turn every mystification into an opportunity to educate ourselves in real history of real science. Following the PM's mystification, the plan calls for looking up our ancient medical to find out what they actually have to say regarding "genetic science" and surgery. When we call them "scientific," what do we mean? If we really had made such advances in medicine in the past, why did we stop? Why has Ayurveda not made any real progress beyond whatever was put down in Charaka and Sushruta samhitas composed in the early centuries of the Common Era?

In this chapter, we will examine these issues in more details. We will first look into the question of "genetic science" in *Charaka Samhita*. The next section will examine the question of plastic surgery, focusing on the method of nose reconstruction in *Sushruta Samhita*. We will follow it up with a comparative history of anatomy where we will address the question why, despite the promising start in anatomy and surgery, we fell behind sister civilizations.

But we will start with a brief discussion of the dangers of anachronistic or "presentist" history. Delving into this problem with history

---

suggestions from them on how to make it relevant for the country." http://www.deccanherald.com/content/461641/education-policy-good-definitely-not.html

To understand why the leadership of Dinanath Batra should worry us, here is a gem from his book, *Bharatiya Shiksha kaa Swarup*: "Charaka explained blood circulation in 300 BC, while the credit is given to William Harvey." p. 50. Batra provides no evidence to back this astounding claim.

8   See Rukmini Shrinivasan, "Medicine Wars," *The Hindu*, April 26, 2015. AYUSH stands for Ayurveda, Yoga, Unani medicine, Siddha and homeopathy. The phrase "alternatives to medicine" was suggested by my friend, Vijayan.

writing may seem like a digression, but its relevance to the issue at hand will soon become evident.

3. Why anachronism is bad history of science

One of the first things all historians are taught to avoid is the "sin" of writing "Whig history", which consists of giving anachronistic or "presentist" accounts of the past.[9] Anachronistic history is simply reading the past in the vocabulary derived from our present knowledge, beliefs, or values. It is "unhistorical history writing" that "studies the past with one eye to the present", to use Butterfield's famous words. Put another way, it uses *now* as the prism through which it views *then*. Historians of science are *especially* wary of presentism for the potential it has to distort what scientists in the past were trying to achieve. The presentist distortion in history of science comes when historians "cast a particular theory, now deemed correct, as proven right from the start," or to put it another way, when they cast the "scientists" of earlier eras as working with the same conceptual and methodological framework as scientists today.[10]

The opposite of anachronistic history is the diachronic, or contextual, history of ideas in which the historian tries to become an observer *in* the past, not just *of* the past; in which the historian takes a fly-on-the-wall approach to writing history. This requires that the historian must

9 The term "Whig history" was made famous by Herbert Butterfield's 1931 classic titled *The Whig Interpretation of History*. By Whig history Butterfield was referring to the habit of British liberals to read the political history of Britain as one long continuous and inevitable march toward parliamentary democracy. This way of history writing worked by reading the contemporary political philosophy of liberalism back into the minds of actors in the past, who in reality may have had totally different motives and meanings for their actions.

10 The quotation is from Douglas Allchin, 2004, p. 182. Strictly speaking, there were no "scientists" before the term was coined by William Whewell in 1834 to describe the students of the knowledge of the material world collectively. By "scientist" he meant an analogue to "artist", as the term that could provide linguistic unity to those studying the various branches of the sciences. But, of course, human beings have been studying the material world from the very beginning of history. The correct name for pre-modern students of nature is "natural philosophers". See Sydney Ross, 1962. See also https://thonyc.wordpress.com/2014/07/10/the-history-of-scientist/

learn to *forget*, or at least learn to disregard, what she or he knows today when interpreting the past.

The reason is obvious: actors in the past did not have access to the conceptual framework that is available to actors living today. This is nowhere made clearer than in the work of Thomas Kuhn, the author of *The Structure of Scientific Revolutions*, a book that radically changed how we think of progress in science. According to Kuhn, "scientists" in the past lived in a different world: *they were not talking of the same things we do today, even when they were investigating the "same" object in the material world.* This creates problems:

> Scientists-historians and those who follow their lead impose contemporary scientific categories, concepts and standards on the past. Sometimes a specialty which they traced from antiquity had not existed as a recognized subject of study until a generation before they wrote. Nevertheless, knowing [from their current state of knowledge] what belonged to it, they [manage to] retrieve the current contents of the specialty from past texts, *not noticing that the tradition they had constructed in the process had never existed.* In addition, they usually treat concepts and theories of the past as imperfect approximations to those in current use, thus disguising the structure and integrity of the past scientific traditions. Inevitably, histories written in this way reinforce the impression that history of science is the triumph of sound method over error and superstition.[11]

The problem with this way of reading the past is that it turns history into a "hall of mirrors", where all we can see is an image of our own present.[12] This is a special problem of science as it turns the sciences of previous eras into *a precursor of, or an anticipation of, what we already know today.* In the process, it continuously updates – or "modernizes" – the achievements of the past. This is how presentism becomes a tool for constructing a glorious past of the nation whose "science" was always "modern".

A couple of examples will help illustrate the problem.

History of science in the West has its share of anachronisms. There is a kind of Hellenophilia among Western historians who think of modern science as a direct descendant of the natural philosophy of Aristotle and Plato. For example, by expressing Aristotle's law of motion in a mathematical equation, it is possible to make Aristotle look like the pre-

---

11 Thomas Kuhn, 1977, p. 149.
12 Carlos Spoerhase, 2008.

cursor of the modern laws of motion described by Newton's three laws, while in reality Newtonian physics could only emerge after Aristotle's natural philosophy was *discarded* root-and-branch.

For an Indian example, consider P.C. Ray's well-known history of "Hindu chemistry". Looking for some evidence that "the Hindus had a very large hand in the cultivation of experimental science", Ray turns to *rasayana* (alchemy) involving the use of mercury and mica that developed sometime between 13th and 14th centuries as part of a tantric practice, the intention of which was to achieve bodily immortality. Ray repeatedly uses "alchemy" and "chemistry" as synonyms, and does not distinguish between the mercury, sulphur and/or mica of the alchemists (who saw these elements as the "seeds" of Shiva and Parvathi respectively), from the modern conception of these elements.[13]

There is no doubt that alchemy involved hands-on work and laid the basis for laboratory techniques like distillation and sublimation that are still used in modern chemistry. But hands-on work by itself does not count as "science". There is no doubt that alchemy *was* the chemistry of middle ages, it was rational and empirical within its theoretical framework. However, that theoretical framework had to be completely *overturned* for chemistry as we know it to emerge.[14] The transition from alchemy to chemistry had already taken place by the close of the 18th century and yet, this break is hard to discern in Ray's work. Presentism allows Ray to celebrate the alchemists as the fathers of chemistry in medieval India, when they were anything but.

P.C. Ray is only the tip of the iceberg; presentism is practically the operating philosophy of modern Ayurveda. The examples are endless: the mysterious *ojas* are transformed into immunity and virility, *prāṇa* becomes "oxygen" and also "energy", while the lotus-like heart that

---

13 Ray, 1918/1992. For a similar critique of Ray, see Pratik Chakraborty, 2000.

14 The paradigm shift did not happen overnight and pioneers of chemistry like Robert Boyle and even the great Isaac Newton continued to practice alchemy. However, these admirers of Francis Bacon were doing alchemy in a scientific spirit, applying the Baconian method of experimentalism to alchemy, and unwittingly began the long process of questioning the idea that elements can be transmuted. Initial continuities gave way to discontinuities between alchemy and chemistry. Just as it is bad history of science to ignore the *continuities* between chemistry and alchemy, it is equally bad history to ignore the eventual *discontinuities*.

sleeps at night and wakes up in the morning become diastole and systole, and so on and so forth. The end result is a schizophrenic mindset which accepts fundamentally contradictory theories about the same subject matter at the same time.[15]

Whereas professional historians of science try their best to avoid presentism, nationalist historians in India have embraced it with a vengeance. Simply reading back whatever we know and value today – which, more often than not, has roots in the post-Enlightenment West – back into ancient times has been the hallmark of Hindu nationalist history. Straight lines of descent from "the Vedas" for everything from science and technology, secularism, democracy, ecological sensibility, etc., abound in this genre of history writing.

4. "Genetic science" in the time of *Mahabharata*

Mr. Modi's claim that "genetic science was present at that time of *Mahabharata*" is a textbook example of anachronistic history. The very idea of "genetic science" in the early centuries of the Common Era when the *Mahabharata* was put together makes no sense outside of the anachronistic history-writing described above.

The concept of a "gene" as a discrete unit of heredity was not known until the beginnings of the 20th century when the work of Gregor Mendel (1822-1884), a Christian monk who lived in what is now Czechoslovakia, was rediscovered. Even the great Charles Darwin (1809-1882), a somewhat older contemporary of Mendel, thought that traits are inherited through the blending of "gemmules" – tiny particles that are shed into the blood by all the cells in the body, which are then "blended" and eventually passed on to the progeny. For example, a tall and a short couple will have children with average height. A parent with blue eyes and a parent with hazel eyes will have children with greyish eyes. Mendel disproved this "blending" theory by meticulously crossing pea plants and

---

15   Wujastyk (2009) cites an interesting example of this schizophrenia. He reproduces a set of model papers from 1990s for the exam required for a degree in Ayurveda. One question is about the variety of "winds" that supposedly move in the blood vessels, while the very next question is about red blood cell counts; question about food getting cooked by *agni* in the stomach is followed by questions having to do with metabolic hormones.

observing how traits (such as color and texture) were passed down to the next generations. It was his tireless and patient work that taught us that genes are passed on as discrete units and do not blend. That these units of heredity sit on the chromosome; that the chromosome is made up of DNA, which has a double-helical structure – these are all later 20th century discoveries.[16]

Strictly speaking, there was no "genetic science" *anywhere* before the concept of genes was invented. That, of course, does not mean that people did not puzzle over *heredity* before they knew what genes were. Indeed, everywhere, in *all* civilizations that we know of, people have tried to understand the process through which some traits run in families; why children resemble their parents and siblings; etc. Just like every other people, ancient Indians pondered the mystery of heredity as well. Their most "scientific" theory – by the standards of that era – is recorded in *Caraka Saṃhitā* (henceforth, *CS*), the foundational text of Ayurveda.

According to Caraka, the birth of any living being involves not two, but *three* partners: the mother, the father, and the soul (the *atman*) attached to its subtle body (*sukshma sharira*), which is looking for a new body after death. Biological parents are necessary but not sufficient, as they only provide the material out of which a body is constructed. The individual soul is a particle of Brahman, the Cosmic Consciousness, which the parents cannot provide. The embryo is a "spirit-matter composite" and therefore ensouled from the moment of its conception.[17] This is how S.N. Dasgupta, the preeminent author of the multi-volume *History of Indian Philosophy* describes the process by which a fetus is formed:

> When a man dies, his soul, together with the subtle body (*sukshama sharira*) composed of the four elements (air, fire, water and earth) in a subtle state, and *manas*, passes invisibly into a particular womb on account of its *karma*, and

16 See James Schwartz (2008) for an interesting history of genetics.

17 As Julius Lipner (1989) correctly points out, because the embryo is considered ensouled from the moment of conception, abortion even at the earliest stages of pregnancy is seen as murder ("hatya") and condemned as a heinous crime at par with killing a Brahmin in the canonical Hindu literature. It is true that women have the right to abortion in modern India, but this law exists in contravention of Hindu ethics.

then, when it comes in contact with the combined semen and blood of the father and the mother, the fetus begins to develop. The semen and the blood operate as causes .....only when they come in connection with the subtle body transferred from the body of a dying being.[18]

Now, this three-party arrangement is *perfectly rational and even necessary* within the classical Vedantic understanding of a human person and what happens at the time of death. In the Vedantic worldview, which *Caraka Saṃhitā* does not question, a human person is made up of gross body (*sthula sharira*), subtle body (*sukshama sharira*) and *atman-Brahman*.[19] The gross body disintegrates at the time of death. The subtle body, which carries all the imprints of deeds and thoughts of the previous life, does not die; it clings to the *atman* of the person who is dying, and together they exit from the gross body. The subtle body continues to live until salvation is achieved, and the *atman* merges with Brahman. Until that happens, it *has* to find a new body after every death.

This, then, is how the physicians who composed the Caraka Samhita understood the process of birth, and the passage of traits from the biological parents, plus the invisible and ethereal subtle body, riding the coat-tails of the eternal atman on its quest for the Brahman.

Though this explanation of conception and birth is coherent within the Vedantic worldview, can it be called "scientific" even within its own context, to say nothing of being scientific in the modern sense of the word? Can we, by any stretch of imagination, claim that "genetic science," or even the idea of heredity, was known to our ancestors?

The answer to both these questions has to be in the negative.

There is no doubt that the Ayurvedic physicians shared the ambitions and the goals of anyone who can be legitimately called a "scientist," insofar as they sought to understand and explain the state of health and disease. Like their modern counterparts they, too, sought to predict and control the course of disease. It is also true that CS encour-

---

18 Dasgupta, Volume II, p. 303. Dasgupta also provides a good description of what happens to the human person at the time of death.

19 The earlier generation of rationalists, notably Debi Prasad Chattopadhyaya, were too eager to find signs of hard empiricism in Ayurveda and claimed that all the Vedic elements (rebirth, e.g.) were later additions to originally materialistic texts. This view is no longer considered valid, as the Vedic elements are knitted into the fundamentals of Ayurvedic writings. See Engler (2003) for one of best critiques of a naïvely rationalist-materialist interpretation.

ages the physicians to use all their sensory faculties to make a proper diagnosis. Yet, empirical observations were made to arrive at conclusions that were untestable, even in theory. In the case of how conception takes place, empirical observations regarding the coming together of father's "seed" (*shukra*, or semen) and the mother's "field" (*sonita*, or blood) were of course made, but were used to simply illustrate the truth of a higher-level concept (the subtle body in search for an "appropriate" womb, for example). The higher-level concept, in turn, was deduced from a divinely sanctioned web of concepts which are seen as "eternally true" and therefore beyond reason and evidence. Independent evidence that may verify or falsify the higher-level concept was neither sought, nor considered proper to seek.[20]

Secondly, CS's argument that the subtle body is a necessary component of conception fails to explain what it sets out of explain – namely, heredity. Any model of heredity must explain how physical and mental traits are transmitted from biological parents to offspring.[21] But according to the long discussion of the process of conception and fetal development found in CS, "the self causes itself to be born by means of itself as an embryo" where self is the eternal soul, the atman. All higher functions which make us human – consciousness, self-knowledge, intelligence, memory, personal identity – are due to the atman that descends into the womb (parents only providing the stuff that the body is

---

20 It has become fashionable these days to argue that science is no different from any local tradition, or from religion and myth, because scientists also operate within a paradigm that they cannot question if they have to do any science at all. It is true that in modern science individual scientists or even communities of scientists at any given time do not challenge the matrix of theories, methods and metaphysical assumptions underlying the science they do; they merely solve puzzles for which they need to accept the assumptions and methods of their paradigm. But the reward structure in modern science has evolved in such a manner that a collective skepticism is encouraged so that the basic assumptions of any paradigm have been tested by the previous generation of scientists. So in science, paradigms do undergo revolutions; there is no guarantee that today's most cherished truths may not join the heap of rejected ideas in the future. Ayurveda on the other hand, "eternalizes" even those empirically tested claims by putting them in the mouth of gods, who passed on this knowledge to human sages, who passed it on to the vaidyas, and so on.

21 Oxford English Dictionary defines heredity as "The passing on of physical or mental characteristics genetically from one generation to another."

made of). The nature of the "mental faculty" of the embryo – whether it is *sattvic*, *rajasic* or *tamsic* – is determined not by biological parents, but by whichever of these traits was dominant in the previous life of the transmigrating soul.[22] It is thus safe to say that CS lacks a complete theory of heredity, as the term is universally understood.

Finally, while the transmigrating soul is a necessary component of ancient "science" of "heredity," it is entirely unnecessary to a modern understanding of genetics. In other words, the soul-stuff can be easily shaved off by Occam's razor with no effect whatsoever on the actual theory and practice on the science of genetics.

Occam's (or Ockhham's) razor is a form of reasoning attributed to William of Ockham, a 14th century Franciscan monk. It simply entreats us to "not multiply entities unnecessarily," where entities are our theoretical assumptions and premises. The rule of thumb that scientists follow is this: a scientific theory that recruits more assumptions, but can stand equally well with less, is needlessly complicated. If there are two theories in the same domain, scientists should accept the simpler one. The logic behind the preference for simpler theories is as follows:

> ..if we can remove the trimmings of unnecessary assumptions and premises without it impacting the quality of the conclusions, then the trimmings are unlikely to play a part in the explanation. As a consequence, they should be dropped as they play no part in the reasoning and thus have no consequence for the conclusion.[23]

To see how it works, ask any of the thousands of molecular biologists in India who continue to believe in karma and rebirth in their personal lives outside work, but do not invoke the soul-stuff in their scientific work. They may not put it these terms, but they are using Occam's razor in the lab, but not outside the lab. In other words, they live

---

22 The mother is said to provide softer tissues like the skin, blood and internal organs, while the contribution of the father is limited to the harder stuff like bones, teeth, hair etc. See Wujastyk, 1998, pp. 95-100. In what amounts to a pathetic clutching at straws, this has been read as an anticipation of the modern human genetics in which the mother contributes the X-chromosomes and the father the Y-chromosomes! See Deb, 2015, p. 84.

23 Quoted from Jason Braithwaite's excellent exposition titled "Occam's Razor: The Principle of Parsimony, available at https://www.academia.edu/1742741/Occams_Razor_The_principle_of_Parsimony

compartmentalized lives; they are hard-core materialists and empiri-cists when they are scientists, yet unquestioningly accept the role that atman plays in matters of life and death in their everyday lives.[24]

To sum up this section: Our ancient medicine does contain a par-tial theory of heredity, but we did not have "genetic science." Our an-cient theory of heredity is of no relevance to modern genetics. It has been shaved off using Occam's razor.

5. Plastic surgery in Ancient India

The Prime Minister's more astounding claim about ancient surgeons doing inter-species head-transplants (as in the case of Lord Ganesh) belongs to the realm of mythology in the sense of "a story ... involving supernatural beings or events," as defined earlier. Such fables are be-yond evidence, and for that reason alone should not be used as evidence for any kind of history. One should let such stories rest in the land of enchantment and imagination where they belong.

Yet, such statements amount to, in football parlance, self-goals by India First team, as they prevent us from seeing the promising begin-nings made by ancient Indian physicians in surgery (this section) and human anatomy (next section).

Any inquiry into surgery and anatomy will naturally start with *Su-shruta Saṃhitā (SS)* which provides a unique window into the world of surgeons and their techniques. The exact dates are hard to pin down, but the scholarly consensus is that the "kernel probably started some centuries BCE, in the form of a text mainly on surgery, but which was then heavily revised and added to in the centuries before 500 CE. This is the form in which we have received the work today."[25] The entire *Saṃhitā* is a work of many hands and contains many historical layers. The text is presented as the teachings of Dhanvantari (identified as the King of Benaras) to his pupil Sushruta.

When admirers refer to Sushruta as the "world's first plastic sur-geon" they are not entirely wrong. Sushruta does describe surgical

---

24 See the first of its kind online survey of the worldview of Indian scientists available at http://commons.trincoll.edu/worldviewsofscientists/report/

25 Wujastyk, 1998, p. 105.

procedures for the reconstruction of the ear, nose and lip for defects; congenital, or acquired. There were ample chances for acquiring these defects, as cutting off someone's nose and/or ears was a common form of humiliation in ancient India, as it was in other ancient societies as well.[26] Apart from reconstructive surgery, there are also descriptions of "ophthalmic couching (dislodging of the lens of the eye), perineal lithotomy (cutting for stone in the bladder), removal of arrows and splinters, suturing, and much besides."[27]

The procedure for nose reconstruction developed by Sushruta is one of undisputable genius. It is described in chapter 16 of the first part of the Saṃhitā. The description is short and essentially consists of the following: The surgeon would take a leaf the same size as the person's deformed nose, and cut a flap of skin from the cheek which had the same measurements as the leaf. This flap would be laid on the tip of the nose, while it is was still attached to the cheek at the other end. Once the cheek flap was joined to the nose, two pipes (probably reeds) would be inserted which would serve as openings for nostrils. Once the skin had "taken" to the nose, its connection with the cheek would be cut. A similar procedure could be used for reconstruction of lips, according to SS. Simple and elegant![28]

There is no doubt that this is the first recorded method for reconstructive surgery in history. It eventually passed into European hands where it was developed further and became the basis of modern plastic surgery of the nose, or rhinoplasty.

But the history of this promising procedure at home in India is rather dismal. While Sushruta's words continued to be copied faithfully in later medical texts, translated into Arabic and reached China, there are no reliable records showing that nose reconstruction or any other surgical techniques described in SS continued to be practiced in India. The birth place of Sushruta had become bereft of anatomical knowledge and surgical practices, so much so that the French traveller Jean-

---

26 Remember what Lakshmana did to Surpanakha? This practice was widespread in ancient Egypt as well.

27 Wujastyk, 1998, p. 106.

28 For a complete description see Wujastyk, 1998, pp. 142-143.

Baptiste Tavernier could write in 1684 that the "natives of this country understand nothing of Chirurgery".[29]

All available evidence (or rather the lack of it) indicates a kind of stagnation which is described by Roy Porter thus:

> Sushruta Saṃhitā maintains that surgery is the oldest and the most useful of the eight branches of medical knowledge... However, there is little evidence to confirm that these practices persisted. A description of the couching operation for cataract exists in the ninth century Kalyāṇakāraka by Ugraditya, and texts based upon Sushruta Saṃhitā copy out the sections on surgery. But medical texts give no evidence of any continuous development of surgical thinking; no ancient or even medieval surgical instruments have survived;[30] nor is surgery described in literary or other sources. ... the early sophistication of surgical knowledge seems to have been an isolated development..[31]

After centuries of complete silence, the Indian method of fixing broken noses was reported in a letter to the editor in the October 1794 edition of *Gentleman's Magazine*, published from London.[32] The letter, signed simply as "B.L." in part says the following:

> Mr. Urban,

> A friend has transmitted to me, from the East Indies, the following very curious, and, in Europe, I believe, a known chirurgical operation, which has long been practiced in India with success; namely, affixing a new nose on a man's face. The person represented in Plate 1 [reproduced below as figure 1] is now in Bombay.

> Cowasjee, a Mahratta of the caste of husbandman, was a bullock-driver with the English army in the War of 1792, and was made a prisoner of Tipu [Sultan] who cut off his nose and one of his hands. In the state of the Bombay army near Seringapatam is now a pensioner of Honorable East India Company. For about 12 months he has remained without a nose when he had a new one put on by a man of the brickmaker caste, near Puna. This operation is now common in India, and has been practiced from time memorial. Two medical gentlemen, Mr. Thomas Caruso and Mr. James Trindaley of the Bombay Presidency, have

---

29 From Wujastyk, 1998, p.108. Chirurgery is an archaic name for surgery.

30 The sketches of instruments – the lion, or crocodile face forceps, knives of various shapes, needles etc. – that abound in modern Ayurvedic books/texts are all artists reconstructions from the descriptions given in the Saṃhitās, and not copies of original and still existing instruments.

31 Porter, 1997, pp. 140-141.

32 *Gentleman's Magazine* started publishing in 1731 and continued to remain in print for the next 200 years. It was the first magazine in the modern sense and has been described as "the 18th century answer to Google". See http://www.otago.ac.nz/library/exhibitions/gentlemansmagazine/index.html

seen it performed as follows…." [A description of the procedure follows which is very similar to Sushruta's method described above].[33]

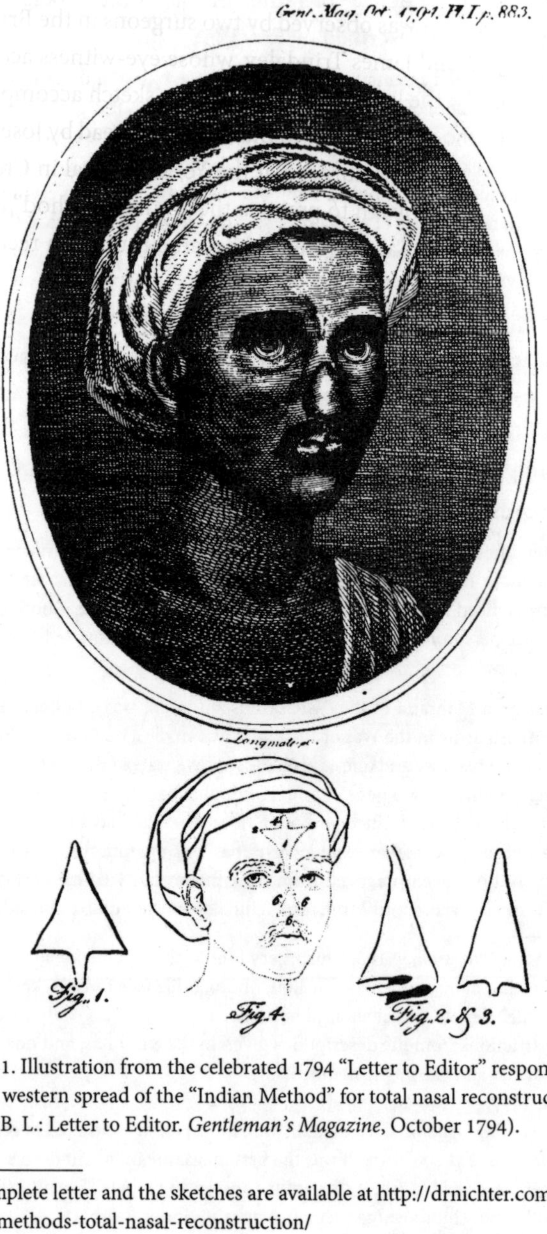
Gent. Mag. Oct. 1794. Pl. I. p. 883.
Longmate sc.
Fig. 1.
Fig. 4.
Fig. 2. & 3.

Figure 1. Illustration from the celebrated 1794 "Letter to Editor" responsible for the western spread of the "Indian Method" for total nasal reconstruction. (From B. L.: Letter to Editor. *Gentleman's Magazine*, October 1794).

33 The complete letter and the sketches are available at http://drnichter.com/impact-indian-methods-total-nasal-reconstruction/

The gist of the story is this: Tipu Sultan cut off the nose and a hand of a bullock-cart driver, Cowasjee, as punishment for working for the British army. He was given a new nose by someone from a "brickmaker" caste. The operation was observed by two surgeons in the British Army, Thomas Caruso and James Trindaley, whose eye-witness account "B.L" was describing in the letter he wrote with the sketch accompanying it.

In all likelihood, this letter to the editor was read by Joseph Carpue (1764–1840), an English surgeon at the York Hospital in Chelsea, who became the first European to practice the "Indian Method" of nasal reconstruction. After that, the method became routine in reconstructive surgery in the West.

The method had to wait for the British to discover it before any further advances could be made. In India itself, there are only hearsay stories of such procedure, but the scientific texts register no improvement over what Sushruta had written many centuries ago.

Why not? Why did medical science come to stagnate after showing so much promise in the beginning?

If we take the PM's call for "regaining" our lost capabilities in medicine, surgery and science in general, it is important to understand the nature of these obstacles to progress of science. Celebrations of ancient science, however well-meant, will not take us far unless we first grapple with what has kept us back all these centuries.

A clue lies in one fact that was noticed by the British observers: those performing this operation were not trained *vaidya*s, but artisan-craftsmen not professionally trained in medicine. In the famous case of Cowasjee reported above, the surgeon came from a family of brick-makers; in another case of cataract removal following Sushruta's method observed in the early 20th century, the surgeon was an illiterate Muslim.

Here we have a classic case of *hand-brain un-coordination*: the brick-maker surgeon and his working-class brethren were ignorant of what was written in Sanskrit texts, while the Sanskrit-trained *vaidya*s had forgotten how to wield a scalpel. Here is how M.S. Valiathan describes the problem:

It is important to note that the procedure in Pune and Coimbatore were not done by Âyurvedic physicians but by illiterate men who had learnt the technique from an earlier generation. They did not understand the anatomical basis of the technique, nor could they explain the rationale for the sequential steps of the procedure. It was as if their brain was uncoupled from their hand movements, which ensured that there could never be innovation based on true understanding.[34]

We explore this split between book-learning and hands-on practice in more detail in the next section. We will see that this split, which largely took place on caste lines, held back progress not just of surgery, but of anatomy as well.

6. Human dissections and anatomy in ancient India

Like geometry (chapter 1) anatomy, too, had its start in Vedic rituals. It is well documented that animal sacrifice was an integral part of Vedic rituals. According to Kenneth Zysk, who has written extensively on healing practices of the Vedic and post-Buddhist eras, "the animals sacrificed were usually cows, but bulls, goats, rams and buffaloes were also offered."[35] The sacrifice of the horse (*Ashvamedha*), however, was considered specially significant and the entire procedure is detailed in the *R̥g Veda* (1.162. 18-20). What is important for our purposes is this: *for the ritual to bring about the desired effect, every aspect of it had to be carried out with extreme precision.* Everything – from the construction of the altar, the recitation of the mantra, from the oblation of exact number of rice balls, to dismembering the sacrificial animal – had to be

---

34 Valiathan, 2006, p. 17.

35 Zysk, 1986. Charles Malamoud, a well-known French Indologist described the procedure for animal sacrifice thus: "first, the creature was strangled or suffocated; then the body was washed by the sacrifice's wife; a special cake was prepared and offered up [to whom?], the carver made an incision above the umbilicus and withdrew the omentum [abdominal membrane]; then he skewered the omentum and grilled it over fire; fragments of gold were inserted into the omentum; the officiants were given their fees; the victim was divided up and unclean parts were offered to demons; the heart was grilled; the other pieces were cooked in a pot; from each joint or portion produced by the division of the body, a small piece was removed for one of the divinities to whom the sacrifice was being offered, and the remainder was distributed to the participants." Quoted here from Wujastyk, 2009, pp. 193-194.

done exactly as laid out in the Brahmana texts. A great misfortune was supposed to befall those involved if the rules were not followed. Even though it was based on superstitious faith in the power of the ritual, the demand for precision led to a considerable knowledge of animal anatomy.[36]

By the time *Sushruta Saṃhitā* appears on the scene, sometime in early centuries of the Common Era, the science of anatomy and surgery had undergone a paradigm shift: it had shifted from the magical and religious rituals of the Vedas to rational-empirical investigation of human body for medical purposes. As M.S. Valiathan put it, in the fifteen centuries that lapsed between the magico-religious practices of *Atharvaveda* to the classical *Saṃhitās*, the "practice of medicine changed from faith-based to reason-based."[37] One crucial sign of this paradigm-shift is *Sushruta Saṃhitā's* advice to aspiring physicians to "remove all doubts by direct observation" and to not rely entirely on the textbooks, or their guru's teachings. This is the beginning of a rational, evidence-based approach to medicine.

It is in this context that "dissections" of dead human bodies makes an appearance in the medical literature.[38] Sushruta recommends the following procedure: the body of a person who died a natural death and has all limbs intact is to be procured and thoroughly cleansed. It is then to be wrapped in a layer of grass and:

> ....placed in a cage or a net in a driving stream in a concealed spot. After seven nights, the completely putrid body should be removed and laid out. Thereupon, one should very gradually scrape off the layers of skin etc. by a whisk made of grass roots. At the same time, every part of the body, great or small, external or internal, beginning with the skin should be *examined with the eye*, one after the other, as it is disclosed in the process of scrubbing.[39] (Emphasis added)

---

36 As Zysk, 1986, p. 689 puts it, "then animal was not cut up for the purpose of scientific observation, as was true in ancient Greece. The action was undertaken for a definite religious goal in mind, but the concern for precision and detail produced a scientific result: a very prudent knowledge of equine anatomy."

37 Valiathan, 2013, p. 5.

38 The conventional meaning of dissection in medicine is "cutting open a dead body into separate parts in order to study it." By this standard, ancient Indians did not dissect, because they did not cut open the bodies they studied.

39 S.S. III.5.50-56. Quoted here from Kutumbiah, 1967, p. 2.

The entire process can be summed up as "see, but don't touch". The eye was to do the examining, while the hand was never to come in direct contact with the decomposed body. A strictly visual examination is better than no examination at all, but it has serious limitations. Because the body is not probed adequately, many internal organs not directly exposed by scrubbing remained unknown to Indian physicians:

- The external and internal structure of the heart and its function was completely misunderstood. Externally, it was described as a "lotus bud" which closes during sleep and opens when awake. (This is interpreted by some as if Sushruta was describing the systole and diastole of the heart!). Internally, it was supposed to have a single cavity, like a tank holding water. There was no conception that the heart contracts; the pulsation in the "ducts" was supposed to be caused by *vāyu* (or air), and not by the heart.

- Virtually nothing was known about the brain and the spinal cord. Both Caraka and Sushruta held that the heart – and not the brain – was the center of sensation, intelligence and consciousness.

- The distinction between arteries and veins was unknown, as was the difference in arterial and venous blood. Since the role of the lungs and respiration was unknown, blood was supposed to acquire its red or bluish color becoming colored differently by different kinds of *rasa* (nutritive juice obtained from food) in the liver or the spleen. The various ducts (*dhamanīs* and *śirās* etc.) were different only in the relative fineness or thickness and they were supposed to originate from the navel, not from the heart.[40]

7. Anatomy in a comparative perspective

Those who adulate ancient Indian medicine must explain the completely erroneous – *by the standards of that era* – understanding of human

---

40   Summarized from Kutumbiah, Engler, Wujastyk.

anatomy described above. Here, we are not comparing ancient Indian knowledge with what we know today, but instead to India's sister civilizations in the centuries spanning the close of the BCE era and the beginning of the Common Era. Once *Sushruta Saṃhitā* is placed in a comparative world perspective, it becomes clear that *Hindu beliefs in purity and pollution hampered the advancement of learning in ancient India.*

Let us look at the Greco-Roman biologists, anatomists, and medical doctors who had no qualms about cutting open and touching the dead bodies of animals, and for a brief period, human cadavers as well. We should start with Aristotle himself (384-322 BCE), the student of Plato (428-348 BCE), the teacher of Alexander the Great (356-323 BCE), and "The Philosopher" of Islamic and Christian theologians and schoolmen until he was dethroned by the Scientific Revolution in the 16th-18th centuries. Unlike in India where the materialists never got a fair hearing, Aristotle provided a perfect balance to the ideal of supersensory transcendental truths sought by Plato and the Pythagoreans. Growing up surrounded by the sea and marine life, this son of a physician began his career as a zoologist. About a fifth of Aristotle's writings that have survived describe some 540 zoological species. Based upon skillful dissections, he described in great detail the inner structure of species ranging from marine animals (dogfish, octopuses, squids), digestive system of ruminants, the eye structure of bees, for example. He is said to have observed the progress of chicken embryos by breaking one egg every day. Early on in the Greek civilization, Aristotle put the study of the living organisms on solid empirical foundations, although he never conducted any studies of the human body.[41]

This tradition of curiosity-driven observations of the natural world culminated in the great strides made in astronomy, geometry and medicine at the great Library and Museum in the City of Alexandria in Egypt. (The city was established by Aristotle's student, Alexander the Great, while the famous Library and the Museum was built by the later line of Ptolemy kings). It is in Alexandria that for a brief period of time, during the third century BCE, dissection of human cadavers was per-

---

41 See David Lindberg, 2007, chapter 3.

mitted. Ancient testimony is unanimous that two medical men, Herophilus of Chalcedon (330-260 BCE) and Erasistratus of Chios (330-255 BCE) undertook systematic dissections of human bodies. They made significant contributions to anatomy, many of which are taught to medical students *to this day*.

Herophilus investigated the anatomy of the brain and the nervous system – exactly those parts which had remained invisible to our "don't touch" anatomists. He is credited with identifying brain membranes (the Dura mater and Pia mater) and tracing the connections between the nerves, the spinal cord and the brain. His detailed description of the human eye has survived to the present day. That's not all: he also identified and described smaller, relatively obscure organs like the pancreas, the prostrate, and Fallopian tubes. He was the first to challenge earlier ideas about arteries carrying air and showed them to be conduits of blood, and also demonstrated that arteries have thicker walls than veins. Erasistratus followed Herophilus, and he is credited with describing the bicuspid and tricuspid valves of the heart, and the role they play in determining the one-way flow of blood. By the time Claudius Galenus, better known as Galen of Pergamon (130-200 CE) appeared as the physician to the Roman emperor Marcus Aurelius, human dissections again were banned. While examining the wounds of the gladiators under his care, Galen was given a chance to observe whatever he could inside the human body. Galen also carried out dissections of animals, including pigs, apes, and even the heart of an elephant. He made impressive gains in understanding heart and blood vessels, as well as the respiratory and nervous systems. (He extrapolated his findings from animals to humans and thus introduced some errors). These achievements remained unmatched until they were challenged over a thousand years later, first by the Arabic physician Ibn al-Nafis (1213-1288) who lived in what is now Syria, and later in 1543 when Andreas Vesalius published his masterpiece, *De Humanis Corporis Fabrica* (or *The Fabric of the Human Body*) based upon public dissections of human bodies in the University of Padua in Italy.[42] (More on him below).

---

42 David Lindberg 2007, Chapter 6. Also, Roy Porter 1997.

This brief foray into Greco-Roman medicine was undertaken for two purposes. The first is simply to set the record straight. As this book has emphasized repeatedly, when we in India make grandiose priority-claims, we have no choice but to place these claims in a comparative world history, otherwise they are mere boasts.

The other aim was to show how Hindu prejudice against pollution literally tied the hands of Indian doctors. After all, why was it that ancient India failed to produce anatomists of the caliber of their contemporaries, Herophilus, Erasistratus, and Galen, whose contributions have endured to the modern era? It is not as if the Greeks had access to superior technology, superior stock of medical knowledge, or superior intelligence. The most important difference was socio-religious; the Greco-Roman surgeons were not burdened with the stigma of being polluted in the sense that their Indian counterparts were. It is not that the Greco-Roman doctors were considered among the social elite, but they were not classified as polluted and unworthy of participating in the religious-cultural life of their society.

Throughout history, everywhere in the world, medical practitioners have occupied an ambiguous social status; their services were needed and even respected, but they have not always enjoyed high social status. In ancient Greece, for example, most medical men came from craft traditions which were held in low esteem by the social elite. In ancient India, the *Ṛg Veda* classified them between carpenters and Brahmins; *Taittirīya Saṃhitā* advised that "medicine is not to be practiced by a Brahman, for he, who is a physician, is impure, unfit for the sacrifice." Only after he had undergone a purification ritual, could a physician be allowed to participate in the *yagna*.[43]

If things were not so great for doctors in the Vedic era, they got progressively worse as time progressed. By the early centuries of the Com-

---

43 This injunction comes from the well-known myth of the Asvins who could put back the head of the sacrificed animal. The Asvins are commanded by the gods to replace the head, but they demand that they be first given a portion of *soma*. Since the gods needed their service, they agreed but only after first purifying the Asvins with *Bhaiṣpavamāna Stotra*. Following this myth, all physicians were to be purified before they could join in a *yagna*. Even though a purification ritual was required of all those participating in a *yagna*, the doctors were treated as a special case. See Zysk, 1998, Chapter 2.

mon Era, rules of purity and pollution got codified into *dharmaśāstra*s, and the stigma of being "impure" kept the medical men out not only from *yagna*s, but from everyday activities as well. According to the law books, dating around the same time as *Sushruta Saṃhitā*, the bearer who carried the corpse to the cremation ground – and by extension anyone who came in contact with a dead body – was deemed to be polluted for a period of three to ten days.[44] *Manusmriti*, the most influential of *dharmaśāstra*s, grouped doctors with those whose touch was polluting, and whose "food was pus".[45] The irony was that from this time onward, "medicine was included among the Hindu sciences and came under Brahminic religious influence", and *Atharvaveda*, the book most relevant to medicine, was given "full authority as an orthodox treatise, alongside other sacred texts of the priestly order and its inclusion served to authorize the medical tradition in the Hindu cultural and religious milieu."[46] Myths were reinterpreted and Vedic pedigrees were invented and superimposed on an already established body of medical knowledge, which actually contradicted many Vedic taboos (on meat eating, for example). Evidence for this Brahminic veneer has been well documented by historians and is now accepted by mainstream scholars who don't have pre-existing biases.[47]

The question necessarily arises: why did purity and pollution acquire such exceptional prominence in India? The answer is complex but not difficult to understand: *purity was the new, post-Buddhist legitima-*

---

44 *Manusmriti*, 5:65. For the exact chapters and verses for other *dharmasūtra*s and shastras including *Gautama, Baudhyāna, Āpastamba, Viṣṇu* and *Pāraskara Gṛhya sūtra*, see Zysk, 1986, p. 692.

45 "The food of a doctor is pus, the food of a woman who runs after men is semen, the food of a money-lender is excrement, the food of an arms-dealer is dirt." *Manusmriti*, 4:220. Doctors were classified with those whose food one must not eat: "hunters, cruel men, one who eats leftovers, a woman who has just given birth and one still within ten days of pollution due to death." *Manusmriti*, 4:212.

46 Zysk, 1998, p. 26.

47 As Kutumbiah (1969, p. i) says: "There was really no Veda called Ayurveda. Its existence is a myth. Sushruta calls it an *upāṅga* of *Atharvaveda*. It was raised to the level of a Veda and appended to the *Atharvaveda* to give the science of medicine the necessary sanctity and authority." The locus classic of unearthing the Hinduization of Ayurveda is Debi Prasad Chattopadhyaya's 1977 book, *Science and Society in Ancient India*.

tion of Brahminic power. The Vedic religion unapologetically saw both nature and society as engaged in a perpetual struggle for existence in which the strong devour the weak: "those that do not move are food for those who move, those that have no fangs are food for those with fangs… and cowards are the food of the brave."[48] Dominance, not purity, was their priority.

However, this civilization that openly celebrated might-is-right, was facing multiple challenges by the beginning of the Common Era: the efficacy of rituals was beginning to be questioned, heterodox seekers (*sramanas*) who no longer believed in the Vedas were growing in numbers. These seekers included Buddhists, Jains, Ajivikas, the Charvakas – and *also physicians and healers*. In response to these challenges the priestly caste began the slow process of co-opting or Hinduizing the ideals of *ahiṃsā* and vegetarianism which were first articulated by the world-renouncers as a way to break the chain between *karma* and rebirth. It is this process through which, to quote Wendy Doniger and Brian K. Smith,

> 'purity'…replaced sacrificial skills as the mainstay of the priest's ideological arsenal. Vegetarianism and non-violence became the principal signifiers of this 'purity' that jostled for power, [and became] the new yardstick for social ranking in the priestly reformation of Vedism.[49]

Given the codification of rules of purity and pollution that were to be followed in every aspect of everyday life from the cradle to the funeral pyre, it was bound to create problems for the *vaidya*s whose work by necessity involved contact with sick bodies. Indeed, it is a sign of their great thirst for knowledge that Indian surgeons did not give up entirely. Scrubbing-and-seeing was too crude a method to tell us much about human anatomy, but the fact that it was undertaken at all is a testimony to the ancient surgeons' thirst for knowledge.

All available evidence suggests that it is thanks to the rise of Buddhism that ancient doctors could come even this far. By now, it is well-established that "the foundations of classical Ayurveda were being laid at the time of early Buddhism in the Buddhist and other ascetic

---

48 *Manusmriti*, 5:29.
49 Doniger and Smith, 1991. 'Introduction' to their translation of *Manusmriti*, p. xxxvi.

communities."[50] The Vedic-age doctors, shunned and denigrated by the priestly class, found refuge in the heterodox communities of wandering ascetics – the *śramaṇas* – who had ceased to believe in the Vedas and were searching for a new path to liberation from the endless cycles of birth, death, and rebirth. One particular *śramaṇic* group, the Buddhists, not only emphasized empirical knowledge, but also made medical care a central part of their monastic life. The first hospitals in India, for example, were established in Buddhist monasteries. Initially, they were meant to care for monks who had no family to look after them. Later, medical care was extended to the lay public as well.[51]

Evidence strongly suggests that Sushruta's method of dissection of human bodies has Buddhist origins. For one, it was a part of Buddhist ascetic practices to contemplate upon decaying bodies to understand the impermanence of the world. *Dīghanikāya*, for example, instructs monks to "reflect upon a putrefying body, dead from one to three days, becoming bloated and decaying, being devoured by animals, until its bones became bleached and turned to powder."[52] Secondly, Buddhists had a custom of disposing the dead body by immersing it into flowing waterbodies. This practice is attested to both by the Chinese Buddhist pilgrim Hsuan-tsang (early 7th century) and by Alberuni (11th century).[53] It is entirely possible (and likely) that some *śramaṇa* physicians combined this contemplative discipline with an interest in medical knowledge, leading to the method described in *Sushruta Saṃhitā*.

---

50 Wujastyk, in Flood, p. 397. The Buddhist influence is accepted by M.S. Valiathan, the doyen of Ayurveda. "In the fifteen centuries which intervened between *Atharvaveda* and *Caraka Saṃhitā*, the stupendous event that transformed India was the advent of Buddhism. It overturned many old beliefs, effaced ancient customs, and subverted social institutions, revolutionized philosophy and enthroned a new species of compassion and brotherhood... Ayurvedic concepts and procedures flourished in Buddhist India, and Buddhists became their foremost exponents. The dominance of Buddhist ideas led to the erosion of Vedic charms and rituals in the management of illness, which became increasingly based on empiricism." (2013, pp. 5-6).

51 See Zysk's 1998 pioneering work.

52 Cited from Zysk, 1998, p. 35.

53 Zysk, 1998, p. 36.

8. The "Ayurvedic Anatomical Man"

Fast forward about a thousand years (give or take a century or two) to the 16th century. What do we find? We find the beginnings of the Scientific Revolution in Europe, while India is in a deep sleep.

Let us first look at India. The prime exhibit is the "Wellcome Ayurvedic Anatomical Man" (Plate 4). It is a work in ink and watercolor, about 2 by 1.5 feet in size, depicting the inside of the human body. This painting is literally one of a kind, as ayurvedic texts are not illustrated, as compared to medical texts from pre-modern China, Japan and Europe. According to Dominik Wujastyk, who has studied this painting in great detail:

> The Ayurvedic Man is an image painted no earlier than 1700, on which have been written extracts from the classic ayurvedic work called *Bhāvaprakāśa* (fl. ca. 1650-1690). The extracts are taken from chapter 3 of the work that deals with anatomy and embryology.[54]

Thanks to Wujastyk's research, we know that the Ayurvedic Man is basically a Nepalese-style diagram of a man, created sometime in the 18th century, with annotations from a 17th century Ayurvedic text called *Bhāvaprakāśa*, written by Bhava Mishra, son of Latakana, probably settled in Varanasi, where he was a renowned physician with 400 students.[55] We know nothing about who commissioned the painting, who the artist was, or who copied the text from *Bhāvaprakāśa* that accompanies the picture. All one can say with any degree of confidence is that it is a co-production between "a rich, perhaps royal patron who initiates the project; a physician who is also a scholar of Sanskrit and Ayurveda; one or more painters of the Citrakāra community, and finally a calligrapher or scribe." Wujastyk infers from his detailed, frame-by-frame and

---

54 Wujastyk, 2008, p. 209. The Wellcome library in London bought this painting in 1986 from an art dealer who specialized in Nepalese artifacts.

55 According to Wujastyk, 2008, p. 206, *Bhāvaprakāśa* "established itself as one of the more important Sanskrit medical texts ever written. Manuscript copies are abundant ... printed editions began to appear from 1855, especially from presses in Bombay and Calcutta. The editions were often accompanied with Hindi, Bengali and Gujarati translations. At least sixteen editions were printed between 1855 and 1998.... This work has remained influential right up to the present time, when it forms part of the standard degree syllabus in Ayurvedic colleges across India." p. 206.

word-by-word analysis that "the scholar was not a great expert in San-skrit texts, and the scribe was apparently ignorant of Sanskrit. Between them, they produced texts that are riddled with errors."[56]

What does the piece and its annotations tell us about the state of anatomical knowledge in medieval India?

The answer in one word: *stagnation.*

The 16th century text used for annotations tells us nothing that Sush-ruta and Caraka would not have known in their time, at least a thousand years earlier. Take for example, what it says about the heart. Exactly what *Sushruta Saṃhitā* said in the early centuries of the Common Era, namely, that the "heart is similar to a lotus, facing downwards. On wak-ing up, it blooms, on sleeping, it closes up. The heart is the resting place for the soul. It is the supreme location of consciousness." Lungs? They are as mysterious to the 16th century physician as they were in Sush-ruta's time. The left and the right lung have different names and "neither is involved in breathing". Kidneys? Well, they come from the "essence of fat and blood. They are said to provide nourishment for the fat in the belly." So on and so forth.[57]

Meanwhile, a revolution was brewing in Europe. In the year 1543 – around the same time when Bhava Mishra was writing his book in Varanasi – two books were published that would transform our knowl-edge of the heavens above and life here on earth.[58]

Nicholas Copernicus, a devout Catholic who managed a Cathedral in Poland, wrote his *De Revolutionibus Orbiusm Coelestium* (or "The Revolutions of Celestial Spheres"), in which he replaced the earth with the sun as the center of the universe, overthrowing at least two thou-sand years of Aristotelian-Ptolemaic astronomy. Andreas Vesalius, a medical doctor and professor at the University of Padua in Italy, came out with his magnificently illustrated *De Humani Corporis Fabrica* (or "the Fabric of the Human Body"), correcting many errors of anatomical knowledge that began in Alexandria and culminated in Galen.

---

56 Wujastyk, 2008, p. 208.
57 All quotations are from Wujastyk, 2008.
58 These are among the first generation of books that were *printed*, not hand-written.

De Humani Corporis Fabrica is a detailed, masterfully illustrated, 600-page book, which is a study of every bit of the human body, based upon dissections of dead bodies which were carried out by Vesalius himself. As the illustrations (plates 5-7) show, Vesalius minutely observed every part of the body – starting from the outer layers, to the muscles, the nervous and the arterial system, the internal organs including lungs, kidneys, the male and female reproductive organs, down to the bare bones of the skeleton. Whatever he exposed through dissection was sketched by the renowned artist, Jan Stephan van Calcar (or Kalkar) of the Netherlands, who had studied with Titian, one of the giants of Renaissance art in Italy. The drawings were carefully etched onto wooden blocks and copperplates – the name of the craftsman who did the engraving remains unknown. The etchings were transported to Basel, Switzerland, where one of the best known printers, Joannis Oporini, set them in print. As the illustarations (plates 5-7) show, apart from being a milestone in medical science, the *Corporis Fabrica* is also a notable example of science, art, and technology coming together.

Placing Vesalius in the larger story of the Scientific Revolution would take us too far from the subject at hand: namely, understanding the growth curve of traditional Indian medicine.[59] For our purpose, what is crucial is to understand the breakthrough that Vesalius made in methodology, which ultimately was made possible because he was prepared to break long-held social taboos.

Vesalius was not the first to dissect human cadavers in the early modern era. The Catholic Church had started allowing autopsies as far back as the 12th century. By the end of the 13th century, professors of medicine (notably, Mondino de Luzzi in University of Bologna in Italy), were using dissections to train medical students. These dissections were carried out in public, with religious and state officials present,

---

59 There is plenty of material on the period known as "medical Renaissance" which included, apart from Vesalius, the important figures of Leonardo da Vinci and Paracelsus. A good resource for history of medicine is Roy Porter's magisterial *Greatest Benefit to Mankind*. The website of the British Library offers a wonderful presentation and explanation of Vesalius's great work in a "virtual book" format, available at http://www.bl.uk/onlinegallery/ttp/vesalius/accessible/introduction.html

along with medical students and members of the general public. The unclaimed bodies of those dying in hospitals and the bodies of executed prisoners were used. As is also well documented, Leonardo da Vinci dissected and drew as many as 30 bodies, including one of a pregnant woman. As he did not have a license from the Church to do this, he was forced to work in secrecy (see plate 8).[60]

Vesalius' genius lay in a methodological innovation that would change medical science forever. Before Vesalius, standard procedure was that the learned professor would sit on a raised podium, read from the works of Galen, the second century Roman surgeon, which had been first translated from Greek into Arabic and later into Latin. Down below him, a lowly surgeon-barber would do the actual cutting and a tutor would point out the organs that the professor was reading about. The result was that even though bodies were being *observed,* they were being *seen* through Galen's book, to the point that what the students "saw" was not actually there.

Vesalius's revolutionary step was simply this: he came down from the podium, took the knife from the barber, and did the messy work of cutting open the body himself. Initially, he too saw what Galen had written – so powerful is the pull of a paradigm – but gradually, he began to see errors in Galen's anatomy, which he had derived from dissections of apes and other animals, not of human beings. Vesalius' innovation changed medicine forever: before Vesalius, medical learning took place through a book; after Vesalius, medical learning took place through the body.[61]

Sociologically speaking, this was unprecedented. Latin-knowing, University trained professors never dirtied their hands; that was left to the lowly surgeons who had the status of barbers. Because he was able

---

60 Da Vinci was assisting a doctor who had the permission from the Church. The doctor passed away while the work was still going on. Da Vinci continued to dissect and draw in secrecy. Toby Huff (2011) provides a good description of history of human dissections in a cross cultural context, including medicine in Islamic lands and in China.

61 I am grateful to Dr. Charleen Moore from the University of Texas Health Science Center for this formulation. It is taken from the lecture she delivered in December 2012 at IISER-Mohali titled "Teaching from the Body or from the Book: Vesalius versus the Establishment".

to bring the theoretical knowledge he had together with what he was observing, Vesalius was able to catch the errors of his predecessors, and in the process revolutionize the study of anatomy. This confirms what is known as "Zilsel's thesis" in history of science. This thesis, put forward by Edgar Zilsel, a socialist philosopher of science who was forced to flee his native Vienna for the United States under the Nazis, argues that the Scientific Revolution in Europe resulted from the lowering of social barriers between craftsmen and scholars.[62]

In light of this comparative history, one can confidently say that the cause of the difference between the growth trajectories of natural sciences in Europe and India was primarily sociological. In early modern Europe, the barriers between scholars and craftsmen were breached from both ends; the more literate amongst the craftsmen began to write in vernacular for their own guild members (and thanks to the printing press, they could do that with relative ease), while the university and seminary educated scholars began to take an interest in the stock of knowledge accumulated by the craftsmen.

In contrast, the lowering of the barrier between scholar and craftsman never happened in India – and it still hasn't to any significant extent. It was outside the realm of possibility that a learned, Sanskrit speaking Vaidya – take the above cited Bhava Mishra for example, who was probably a contemporary of Vesalius – would do what Vesalius did without losing his caste, being excommunicated, and having to undertake many rituals of atonement and purification.

Given what we know now, we can only conclude that the ancient Indians' obsession with pollution and purity killed off the spirit of empirical, evidence-based investigation of the natural world.

9. Conclusions

We do have lessons to learn from our ancient heritage. But these lessons don't have anything to do with what we actually knew, or how we went

---

62 See Zilsel (2000) for Edgar Zilsel's historic paper written in 1942. Zilsel's thesis has played an influential role in the history of science. It inspired Joseph Needham's classic history of science in China. It has inspired a host of recent books, including Clifford Conner's *A People's History of Science*.

about knowing what we knew. The real lesson of the history of medicine in India is negative; it tells us what stifled the development of medical and other empirical sciences in India. The history of medicine (indeed, history of all natural sciences in India) is less of a source of inspiration than a cautionary tale regarding the evils of social hierarchy legitimized by superstitions.

We cannot "regain" the "capabilities" which we never had to begin with. Yet, history of medicine – the real thing, not the fake one manufactured from myth and legend – is worth studying, for it can teach us what *not* to do if we are really serious about building real capabilities in medicine and science in general.

Chapter 4

Yoga Scientized

How Swami Vivekananda Rewrote Patanjali's *Yoga Sūtra*

Those who have one foot in the scientific and the other in the religious domain risk losing their foothold in both. Wouter Hanegraaff.

1. Introduction

Just over 120 years ago, on September 19, 1893 to be precise, Swami Vivekananda stood before the World Parliament of Religions in Chicago.[1] In his much-celebrated Chicago address, he declared Hinduism to be a religion that is fully validated by modern science: "what the Hindu has cherished in his bosom for ages", to use his words, "is going to be taught in more forcible language, and with further light from the latest conclusions of science". "Modern science is but an echo of the spiritual flights of Vedanta philosophy", he declared.[2]

After Chicago, Vivekananda spent time in and around New York where he gave a series of lectures on Patanjali's *Yoga Sūtra*. These lectures, along with Vivekananda's translation and commentary on the

---

1 The year 2013 marked the 120th anniversary of Vivekananda's famous Chicago address and the 150th anniversary of his birth. By sheer chance, a much shorter version of this chapter was read at a conference on modern yoga at the University of Vienna on September 20, 2013, missing the 120th anniversary by a day.

2 *Complete Works of Swami Vivekananda*, the Mayavati edition in 8 volumes (Henceforth *CW*), vol. 1, p. 15. Interestingly, Vivekananda was not the only Asian invoking science at Chicago. Equally eloquent were Anagarika Dharmapala from Sri Lanka and Soen Shaku from Japan who declared *Buddhism* to be the most scientific of all religions. See McMahan (2010).

original text were put together as a book titled *Raja Yoga*. Published in 1896, *Raja Yoga* introduced yoga philosophy to Americans, and proved to be hugely popular. The yoga of *Raja Yoga* is *not* the yoga of *asana*s, or bodily postures, for which the Swami had nothing but disdain.[3] Rather, by yoga Vivekananda meant the yoga of *samadhi*, the meditational yoga taught by Patanjali, circa first century of the Common Era.

In this book, Vivekananda extended the rhetoric of science to yogic meditation. In his Chicago address, Vivekananda had argued that the religion of the Hindus is "scientific" as it does not accept any dogmas on faith, but accepts *only what can be verified by experience* – which is the hallmark of empiricism. "The Hindu religion", Vivekananda had declared, "does not …believe in a certain doctrine or dogma…" and "the Hindu does not live upon words and theories", but only accepts what he can "directly see" for himself:

> If there are existences beyond the ordinary sensuous existence, the Hindu must come face to face with them. If there is a soul in him which is not matter, if there is an all merciful universal Soul, he must *go to Him direct*. He must *see* Him and that alone can destroy all doubts. So the best proof that a Hindu sage gives about the soul, about God, is: "I have seen the soul; I have seen God." (*CW*, vol. 1, p. 13, emphases added).

It is through yoga that "the Hindu" comes face-to-face with the Universal Soul. "The science of *Raja Yoga*", he told his disciples, "proposes to put before humanity a practical and scientifically worked out method" which will allow everyone to directly see "the ever-lasting soul within" (*CW*, vol. 1, p. 128). For Vivekananda, then, *Hinduism is a rational religion, a religion of science, and yoga is its "scientific method", its method of verification.*

2. Scientism and Hindu nationalism

If his claims of super-sensuous, yogic "seeing" were limited to spiritual enlightenment – some form of "scientific religion", or "rational mysticism" that does not require a belief in a supernatural God – there would be no need for this chapter. But Vivekananda is making a much bigger

---

3   *Haṭha yoga* can make you healthy and live long, but "[T]hat is all… so if a man lives long, he is only a healthy animal" because this yoga "does not lead to much spiritual growth." (*CW*, vol. 1, p. 138).

claim which boils down to this: *Yoga is "scientific" in a more robust sense of providing empirically verifiable knowledge and control of the material world through access to the spiritual world that it provides.* When mysticism steps into the domain of natural science in such an overt manner, it is practically begging to be challenged – and this chapter intends to oblige.

Vivekananda opened the door to a form of scientism which has served Hindu supremacist ends from the day it was enunciated. Every exponent of yoga after Vivekananda – from the erudite philosopher-statesman, S. Radhakrishnan to yoga gurus like Parmahansa Yogananda of Self-Realization Fellowship, Swami Sivananda of Divine Life Society, Maharishi Mahesh Yogi of TM (Transcendental Meditation) and his disciple, Deepak Chopra – has indulged in copious amounts of science-talk to lend a sheen of authority to their exposition of yoga philosophy and practice. Yogic meditation, after Vivekananda, has become a matter of controlling and manipulating the "*prāna* " or the "vital energy" of the cosmos – a form of "energy" that is simultaneously a "spiritual" emanation of the divine, *and* a physical entity that obeys the laws of physics. Even though every effort of modern physics and biology has failed to detect this divine, self-aware "energy", Vivekananda's pairing of spirit with energy, and Hinduism with modern science, has acquired a life of its own.

It is fair to say that scientism – understood here as "adopting the manners, the trappings, the technical terminology of the sciences, irrespective of their real usefulness"[4] – has become the dominant episteme of modern yoga and indeed, of contemporary Hinduism itself. It has become a part of the common sense of the educated, upwardly mobile segments of Indian society that there is "no conflict" between science and Hindu beliefs about the natural world, soul, evolution etc., and that modern science has only reaffirmed what their Vedic ancestors already knew. As Agehananda Bharati, the great Austria-born Hindu monk and anthropologist put it, the mark of the Hindu modern is to argue that "'X = scientific' – and hence by implication 'modern', where X can be any trait linked to the Indian tradition."[5]

---

4   Susan Haack, 2009.
5   Bharati, 1970, p. 273.

There is a need to deconstruct this illusion of harmony between any and all "Xs linked with the Indian tradition" with whatever happens to be the consensus theory in modern science at any given time because it distorts both: It robs the X of its spiritual-cultural meaning, while robbing modern science of its distinctive methodology and worldview. While this illusion may boost our national pride, it can only create a culture that lacks any core beliefs whatsoever. If we continue down this path, we will neither retain our distinctive spiritual beliefs, nor develop habits of critical thought required for doing good science. For, to repeat Wouter Hanegraaff's wise words quoted above, "those who have one foot in the scientific and the other in the religious domain risk losing their foothold in both."

Any such deconstruction has to begin with a serious look at Swami Vivekananda's corpus of writings in which he turns modern science into a mere "echo" of Vedanta. The Swami is central, for he pioneered this genre of scientism in modern India. He is also central as he has been appropriated as their icon by the Sangh Parivar.

The association of the Sangh Parivar with Vivekananda and Ramakrishna Mission did not begin with candidate Narendra Modi dressing and posing like the "other Narendra." [6] It is well known that Modi himself and other leaders of RSS including Guru Golwalker had wanted to become monks in the Rama Krishna Mission, but found their true calling in the RSS. [7] At a time when Swami's words are quoted as their

---

6 The following from *India Today* (Jan 12, 2012) deserves an extended quotation: "As part of the BJP's election strategy, party members have found a novel method to promote Narendra Modi as a champion of saffron power. On Jan. 12, a vernacular daily carried a quarter page advertisement – issued by one of the district presidents – which sought to draw a parallel between Modi and his namesake Swami Vivekananda whose real name was Narendra Dutta. It featured both of their pictures side by side, with Modi sporting attire similar to Vivekananda's – a saffron turban with a shawl. A message alongside the images, with Modi mirroring Vivekananda's posture read: 'it is a river of saffron color, of which Narendra (Vivekananda) is on one bank and Narendra (Modi) is on the other. Let us all soak in the great flow of nationalism and commitment to nation building flowing between these two banks.'"

7 As a young man, Narendra Modi wanted to become a monk in the Rama Krishna Mission but was advised that his calling lay in politics. See http://timesofindia. indiatimes.com/city/kolkata/Modi-wanted-to-be-Ramakrishna-monk-rejected-

guiding light by educationists, policy makers and even Supreme Court judges, it becomes imperative to read Vivekananda carefully.[8]

3. Questions before us

In this chapter, I want to take a closer look at the hermeneutics of Vivekananda's scientized yoga: How is the language of specific scientific theories of physics and biology appropriated? How is yogic meditation made to appear as "just like" scientific empiricism, but only better? How are the paranormal yogic *siddhi*s (levitation, remote seeing, entering someone else's body, for instance) defended while claiming "no conflict" between yoga and established principles of physics and biology? How is this alchemy of meaning made convincing enough for the educated lay audiences in the modern world?

I will examine these questions by a careful reading of Swami Vivekananda's *Raja Yoga* – the founding text of modern yoga. I will argue that *Raja Yoga* is made up of layers-upon-layers of "resemblance thinking", a style of thinking which is recognized in philosophy of science as a major source of pseudo science. I will shortly clarify what exactly I mean by resemblance thinking. For now, we can characterise it as a style of thinking through analogies or correspondences of a special kind. This style of thinking is deeply entrenched in the Vedic tradition (as indeed, it was in the ancient and medieval cosmologies in the Christian West, before the Scientific Revolution starting in the 16th century utterly discredited it.)

I will argue that *Raja Yoga* offers us a complex, multi-layered tapestry woven out of resemblance thinking. What we find in *Raja Yoga*

---

thrice/articleshow/19468165.cms. For a brief history of the long-standing relations between the RSS and Vivekananda and R. K. Mission, see Pralay Kanungo, 2013, and also Jyotirmaya Sharma, 2007.

8   See http://dharmalaw.blogspot.in/2010/01/impact-of-swami-vivekananda-on.
    html for a summary of Supreme Court judgements which quote Swami Vivekananda. For a look at the influence of a think-tank associated with Vivekananda Kendra, see http://www.business-standard.com/article/specials/in-the-right-place-114060601203_1.html. For an overview of what the nation's vice-chancellors think of Vivekananda's place in education, see http://samvada.org/2013/news/full-report-national-conference-of-vice-chancellors-by-swami-vivekananda-150-samiti-in-delhi/

are the *ancient* correspondences (or *bandhus*) of Vedic provenance which posit resemblances between the microcosm and the macrocosm, wrapped up in *modern bandhus* that Vivekananda invents between the Vedic *bandhus* and modern science. In other words, *Vivekananda offers us the old occult worldview of Yoga Sūtras dressed up in fancy clothes of science*. He accepts and even celebrates the magical associations established through yogic practices, but simply overlays upon them a vocabulary of mechanical cause-and-effect derived from Newtonian physics. He accomplishes this hybridization of yoga and science by drawing analogies and resemblances between the two – a method which has a long and unchallenged lineage in all of orthodox Hindu schools of philosophy.

Here is a thematic map of how this thesis will be argued:

First, I will read Vivekananda's scientization of yoga through insights emerging from cognitive science that explain how resemblance-thinking generates pseudo science. The two cognitive scientists whose work I will refer to are: Paul Thagard, a well-respected computational philosopher of science from Canada, and Daniel Kahneman, a psychologist who won the Nobel Prize for Economics in 2010.

Secondly, I will place *Raja Yoga* in the confluence of Theosophy and other spiritualist movements that were popular in the cultic milieu of the 19th century United States. I will suggest that modern Hinduism is as much "Theosophized", as it is "Semiticized", as has been argued by Romila Thapar and others.[9] There is sufficient historical evidence to show that the *inspiration* for "syndication" or consolidation of Hinduism under one Bible-like book (the Gita), one Vatican-like mandir (the Ram-mandir in Ayodhya), claims of historicity of Krishna and Rama, concern with social welfare activities, does come from monotheistic faiths, especially Christianity. But the *actual method* or *style of reasoning* used to re-interpret the orthodox Hindu worldview – the "neo" in neo-Vedanta and neo-Yoga – bears all the hallmarks of Theosophy.[10] One

---

9 Thapar, 1991, p. 159.

10 The Oxford English Dictionary defines "theosophy" as "any of a number of philosophies maintaining that a knowledge of God may be achieved through spiritual ecstasy, direct intuition, or special individual relations [with the divine]", http://www.oxforddictionaries.com/definition/english/theosophy. We will, however,

tell-tale sign of Theosophization is the almost obsessive concern with "harmonization" of ancient cosmology of Hinduism with Darwinian evolution and with scientific laws of physics as applied to energy. As we will see, not only does Vivekananda share the Theosophists' impulse to scientize the *Yoga Sūtras*, he ends up using similar arguments and similar analogies as one finds in the Theosophical literature of his times.[11]

Finally, I will argue that the neo-Hindu obsession to connect every new idea – including (or especially?) modern science – to "the Vedas" is *itself* Vedic in inspiration. Holding "the Vedas", broadly defined, as the archetype of all valid knowledge to which all post-Vedic, non-Vedic, or indeed, non-Indic truth-claims must be reconciled, has long served as a "strategy for orthodoxy", to use Brian Smith's words.[12] Indeed, Vivekananda's writings are a perfect example of this "strategy for orthodoxy". I will conclude with some reflections on the dangers of the kind of scientism that Vivekananda made fashionable in India.

4. Postmodernist "cyborgs"

Others before me – most notably Joseph Alter, Brian Hatcher, Anantanand Rambachan, and McKenzie Brown – have noticed the streak of scientism that runs through the writings of Vivekananda and other pioneers of modern yoga. But many of these scholars tend to treat the science-talk of modern yoga with a postmodernist indulgence:[13] It is not the truth-content or the evidential basis, but the politics of Orientalism that they have largely concentrated upon, which follows logi-

---

use theosophy with a capital "T", referring to the doctrines of the Theosophical Society, founded in 1875 by Helena Blavatsky and Henry Steel Olcott. Though it was born in the New York City, the Theosophical Society set up its headquarters in Adyar, Madras (now Chennai) in the early 1880s.

11   The influence of Theosophical Society on the intellectual milieu of the 19th c. Hindu Renaissance has not received the attention it deserves. Kathryn Tidrick (2006) has made an important beginning by looking at the influence of Theosophy and esoteric Christianity on Gandhi. De Michelis (2004) has taken the lead in exploring the influence of Western esotericism on Vivekananda.

12   Brian Smith, 1998, p. 23.

13   Rambachan and Brown are exceptions. Rambachan is troubled by Vivekananda's parallelism between spiritual knowledge and science, while Brown is skeptical of scientism.

cally from their stance towards objectivity, truth and evidence as being socially constructed and therefore relative to the social context.[14] For the post-ist critics, the mere fact that Indian thinkers at the cusp of India's freedom turned to modern *"Western"* science to make sense of their own cultural inheritance is enough to paint them as having accepted the colonizer's mental categories, thereby carrying on the project of colonialism-without-colonizers. But what they fail to see is that the thinkers of the Indian Renaissance were appropriating so-called "Western" science to bolster their own heritage, despite serious and obvious contradictions. The vitalist worldview that animates Vedanta and yoga, to take just one example of the contradictions, was under a serious challenge in "Western" science at the close of the 19th century (and stands totally discredited today).[15] And yet, Vivekananda and those following him, accepted it unquestioningly, and tried to bolster it using spurious arguments based on nothing but analogies. Just because Indian thinkers turned to "Western" science does not make them colonized by the West: it is how they understood science and the use they made of it that matters.

It is not just the postmodernist left has shown undue indulgence toward neo-Hindu eclecticism, the traditional secular left, too, has shown undue eagerness to count Swami Vivekananda as one of their own. For once, I agree with Arun Shourie who challenged the left's newfound adoration for the Swami in the following words, written in 1993:

> The central premise of Swami Vivekananda's entire life was that the essence of India lay in religion; that the religion of our people was the Hindu dharma; that this was not just a lever with which India was to be reawakened, the truths that the Hindu seers had uncovered were the goals to which that reawakened India

14 In Nanda (2004), I have taken an oppositional stance toward social construction of scientific knowledge. I was associated with Alan Sokal and other scientists and philosophers of science who opposed the fashionable doctrines of social constructivism in the so-called "Science Wars" that consumed the American academy through the late 1990s.

15 The *Routledge Encyclopedia of Philosophy* defines vitalism as a doctrine that "living organisms are fundamentally different from non-living entities because they contain some non-physical element or are governed by different principles than inanimate things." Vitalism has zero credibility among professional biologists today, although it continues to live a charmed life in all kinds of New Age techniques of "pranic healing," "chi", "therapeutic touch," "energy medicine" etc.

had to be turned, and these truths were that pearl of inestimable value which it was India's mission to give to the rest of the world. Which red-blooded Communist or secularist will own up to this credo?[16]

We will not pursue the traditional left's readings of the Swami any further, as this chapter is mostly about the eclectic style of hybridizing science and Hinduism that began with Vivekananda and continues be the dominant style of Hindu nationalist writings on science. In the context of this essay, the post-modernist legitimation of hybridity is of greater concern than any ham-handed attempts to appropriate Vivekananda for a secular-progressive agenda. A couple of examples will clarify what I mean by post-modernist legitimation of hybridity.

In his well-known book *Yoga in Modern India*, Joseph Alter describes at great length the work of Swami Sivananda and Swami Kuvalayananda, key figures in modernizing the yoga tradition in the first half of the 20th century. He describes how they created equivalences between *yogic science* as a technique for realizing ultimate Truth, and *modern science* as a precise mode of experimentation to arrive at provisional but warranted truths. But Alter simply celebrates this conflation as a "cyborg", a symbol of postcolonial hybridity that denies the standard dualities between, "nature and culture, organic and inorganic, animal and machine and [last but not the least] truth and fiction, science and pseudo science".[17] Likewise, Brian Hatcher, who has written an entire book on the eclecticism of modern Hinduism, ends up justifying Vivekananda's propensity to find "a likeness of totally unlike things", as the "right of a colonized people to make their own rules as they go along" and to "fit the facts" to the needs of creating a new national identity. In Hatcher's narrative, Vivekananda emerges as a master *bricoleur* who heroically and fearlessly took whatever he needed, from wherever he could get it, to build a new "homely home" for Hinduism that practically radiated science, hard-nosed empiricism, reason, evolutionary progress, a muscular manliness – in short, all the values that the West celebrated and found lacking in the East.[18]

---

16   Arun Shourie, 'Myths about the Swami', available at http://arunshourie.bharatvani. org/articles/19930131.htm

17   Alter, 2004, p. 41.

18   Hatcher, 1999, p. 157 and passim.

Such postcolonial defenses accept the fashionable social construc-
tivist position that all standards of rationality are internal to cultures/
paradigms, and therefore there are no neutral criteria for demarcating
science from pseudo science: all such boundary-work ultimately depends upon socio-political interests and cultural assumptions of those
drawing the line.[19] The standard narrative goes as follows: The colonial
powers declared the local knowledge of the colonized peoples as non-
scientific and mythic in order to destroy their knowledge-traditions –
and thereby destroy their self-respect, self-confidence and creativity.
Now, it is the turn of postcolonial subjects to turn the tables, disregard
the science-non-science boundary – which was always political any-
ways – and create hybrid worldviews which enable them to live in the
modern world at their own terms.

With due respect, scholars who have looked at modern yoga
through the lens of post-marked theories have cherry-picked what they
want from wider debates in philosophy of science. Social constructivism is by no means the last word on the nature of science: on the contrary, starting with Alan Sokal's well-known hoax, social constructivism
has come under serious critique.[20] The search for a principled, but more

---

19   Postmodernism goes much beyond the traditional historicist claim that all inquiry
     is influenced by the values and interests of the inquirer. What is distinctive about
     the postmodernist/social constructivist turn – and why it is important to reject
     it – is the claim that *the very criteria* demarcating truth and falsity, science from
     myth or ideology, empirically verified facts from superstition are constructed dif-
     ferently by different cultures and there is no *rational* reason for choosing one over
     the other. The only reason science is deemed universal and objective is that it is
     backed by the power of the West over the Rest. For a clear and concise statement
     of what is wrong with postmodernism, see the essay Paul Boghossian wrote in the
     immediate aftermath of the "Sokal Affair" in 1996. This essay is re-reproduced
     in Noretta Koertge's *A House Built on Sand*, an anthology of essays in support of
     Sokal's demonstration that the postmodern turn in understanding science is an
     emperor with no clothes on.

20   In its 1996 Spring/Summer issue, the journal *Social Text* published a paper by
     Alan Sokal, a professor of physics at New York University. Titled 'Transgressing
     the Boundaries: Towards a Transformative Hermeneutics of Quantum Gravity',
     this essay, close to eighty pages in length, went about deriding the "Enlightenment
     biases" of "'objective' procedures and epistemological strictures prescribed by the
     so-called 'scientific method'" and called for a new "emancipatory" mathematics
     that would "liberate" physics and society from the hegemony of patriarchal, capi-
     talist, Western "objective" science. This essay, which is actually a hilarious parody

nuanced line of demarcation between objective science and pseudo science than the one proposed by Karl Popper has continued. One such nuanced profile of pseudo science comes from Paul Thagard, to which I turn next.

5. The conceptual profile of pseudo science

Let me very quickly define my terms:

By *science* I mean: those bodies of knowledge that we take to be most solidly grounded in evidence, critical experimentation and observation, and rigorous reasoning. To paraphrase Alan Sokal, the two most notable features of scientific methodology are its *critical spirit* – that is, a commitment to put your beliefs to stringent tests and revising or discarding those ideas that fail the test; and *fallibism*, that is, the understanding that all our knowledge is open to revision in the light of better evidence.[21]

My understanding of *scientism* comes closest to Olav Hammer's definition: Scientism is "an active positioning of one's own claims in relation to the manifestations of any of the academic scientific disciplines, including … the use of scientific terminology, technical devices, references to theories, mathematical calculations etc… *without*, however, actually subjecting your claims to the methods approved within the scientific community."[22] For example, the 1998 "Ig Nobel" prize winner, Deepak Chopra's "spiritual laws of success" by themselves are not scientistic, but they *become* scientistic when they are "actively positioned" in terms of quantum physics.[23] Creation stories from the Vedas

---

of the postmodern style of using big words, vague parallels and non-sequiturs, was accepted for publication in a special issue of *Social Text* that was devoted to the defense of a postmodern turn in science studies. After it was published, Sokal revealed to the journal *Lingua Franca* that his essay was a hoax which he had concocted to see "would a leading journal of cultural studies publish an article liberally salted with nonsense if a. it sounded good, and b. it flattered the editors' ideological preconception?"

21 Sokal, 2006, p. 287.

22 Hammer 2004, p. 206.

23 The 1998 "Ig Nobel" prize in physics was awarded to "Deepak Chopra of The Chopra Center for Well Being, La Jolla, California, for his unique interpretation of quantum physics as it applies to life, liberty, and the pursuit of economic happi-

are creation *stories*, but they become "Vedic creationism" or "scientific creationism" when geological evidence or fossil records are interpreted as if they support these stories.[24]

Pseudo science is simply fake science. It is a "science" that dares not speak its own name. Just as no adherent of a religious doctrine calls himself a "heretic", no one ever identifies himself or herself as a "pseudo-scientist".[25] What is distinctive about the claims which are labelled "pseudo science" is that it "tries to gain legitimacy by wearing the trappings of science, but fails to abide by the rigorous methodology and standards of evidence that demarcate true science. Although pseudo science is designed to have the appearance of being scientific, it lacks any of the substance of science."[26]

The connection between scientism and pseudo science is clear: *scientism – as purposive, active positioning of one's claims in the light of modern science – is how pseudo science is generated.* One great advantage of this understanding of scientism is that rather than look for essential features that will, once and for all, demarcate properly scientific claim from non-scientific or pseudo-scientific claim, it allows for the attitude, agency and political purposes. It is the "active positioning" by historically-located agents that make a claim appear scientific, or not.[27]

---

ness." According to Wikipedia, "Ig Nobel Prizes are a parody of the Nobel Prizes and are given each year in early October for ten unusual or trivial achievements in scientific research. The stated aim of the prizes is to "honor achievements that first make people laugh, and then make them think". The same year Chopra was "honored", the Ig Nobel for Peace went to "Prime Minister Shri Atal Bihari Vajpayee of India and Prime Minister Nawaz Sharif of Pakistan, for their aggressively peaceful explosions of atomic bombs."

24 For a "Vedic alternative to Darwin's Theory" of evolution, see Michael Cremo, 2003. The book is a compendium of paranormal beliefs derived from Hinduism and presented as a theory of evolution. Cremo is a member of ISKCON and writes on matters of natural sciences from a Krishna Consciousness perspective.

25 To quote Michael Gordin (2012, p.1): "There is no person who wakes up in the morning and thinks to himself, 'I'll just head to my pseudolaboratory, do some pseudoexperiments to try to confirm my pseudotheories with pseudofacts.' As is surely obvious, pseudo science is a term of abuse, an epithet attached to certain points of view to discredit these ideas."

26 Quoted here from Rational Wiki at http://rationalwiki.org/wiki/Pseudoscience.

27 For a recent survey of non-essentialist and contextualist attempts at demarcating science proper from pseudo science, see Martin Mahner, 2007.

At this point, let me introduce the work of Paul Thagard, who is widely regarded as a pioneer in what is called computational philosophy of science and who has written extensively on the role of analogical thinking in science. In their book titled *Mental Leaps*, Thagard (and his co-author Holyoak) argue that finding analogies, parallels or resemblances – what they call "mental leaps" – between something that is already known and familiar to us (*the source domain*), to something that is new, unfamiliar and puzzling (*the target domain)* is a fundamental mechanism for making sense of the new and the unknown. Human beings and other higher mammals seem wired for analogical thinking. There are no hard-and-fast rules of logical deduction that dictate these mental leaps, but they are not entirely haphazard either: analogies are guided by noticing some kind of rough similarity in the actual content, structure and/or the imagery, rhetoric and metaphoric content of two otherwise different domains.

Both science and religions propose *unobservable* things which make sense by analogy with things that we can *observe*. Thus, the invisible, all-powerful God makes sense as the heavenly analogue of father here on earth, and the invisible all-pervasive Brahman or Consciousness makes sense as the salt dissolved in water which is in every particle of the water and yet invisible to the eye. History of science, likewise, is replete with many well-known examples of scientific discoveries starting out as analogies which, "like sparks that jump across gaps",[28] carry an idea from one domain to another. Some examples: Galileo defended Copernicus' idea that the earth moves around the Sun by comparing the earth to the moon he observed from his telescope: if a big dense rock like the moon can orbit around the earth, there is no reason why the Earth couldn't move; Newton made an analogy between a planet and a stone thrown from the earth with greater and greater force to argue that the laws that applied to the stone can also explain the motion of planets; Benjamin Franklin explained lightening by comparing it with electrical phenomena. My personal favorite is how Charles Darwin arrived at his theory of natural selection by seeing an analogy with artificial selection performed by animal breeders, and how he figured

---

28 Quoted here from Holyoak and Thagard, 1995, p. 7.

out the basis for natural selection by seeing a likeness between Thomas Malthus's tract on human population and the struggle for existence in nature. These analogies, of course, played a largely heuristic role in the discovery process: Darwin spent nearly 20 years collecting evidence to test the analogy and to support his claim that nature can produce new species by selecting those better adapted in the struggle for existence. *While both religion and science use analogies, scientific theories, unlike religions, must eventually evaluate the theories inspired by analogies in relation to observable evidence*: that is the essential difference between science and religion.

Analogical thinking has a shadowy twin that leads not to science but to pseudo science. Thagard calls it "resemblance thinking" and defines it as "a style of thinking that infers two things are *causally related* from the fact that they are *similar* to each other."[29] This, he says, is the chief culprit behind pseudo science.

What does this statement mean? Why is it that inferring *causality* from *similarity* turns analogical thinking from a source of creativity in science to a source of fake-science?

The problem of inferring causality from similarity is that it adds many unwarranted layers of meaning and significance to a relationship based on nothing more than a surface similarity. *Inferring causality from similarity means that objects or processes which look and feel similar to each other are deemed to act upon each other, and upon the rest of the world, in a like manner.* Therefore, by understanding one, you automatically think you understand the other, and by controlling one, you automatically get to control the other. No more laborious testing and falsification is needed. Thus, the evidential basis of genuine science, acquired through hard work, gets transferred to untested claims based upon nothing more than an analogy.

A classic example goes as follows: gold among the metals is like (in color and significance) the sun among the planets, or like the heart within the body. Because of the metaphorical similarity between the sun and gold, wearing gold next to the heart is supposed to attract beneficial energy of the sun to the heart. Or, take another example: the red-

---

29 Thagard 1988, p. 162, emphasis in the original.

dish cast of the planet Mars resembles the color of blood and that is the reason Mars is supposed to cause bloodshed, wars and aggression and the "pretty" Venus is associated with beauty and motherhood. Resemblance thinking is what makes people think that redheads are short tempered, that those with a bad handwriting are disorderly, those with large foreheads are smarter, those with long "lifelines" on their palms live longer etc. Such relations are based entirely on superficial similarities, rather than on any correlations based upon rigorous, double-blind studies.

To sum up, Thagard does not give a necessary and sufficient demarcation principle, but a historically located profile of pseudo science. In his most recent writings, Thagard (2010) has improved upon his earlier work, and offered the following profiles of science and fake science:

1. Science explains using mechanisms, whereas pseudo science lacks mechanistic explanations.
2. Science uses correlation thinking, which applies statistical methods to find patterns in nature, whereas pseudo science uses dogmatic assertions, or resemblance thinking, which infers that things are causally related merely because they are similar.
3. Practitioners of science care about evaluating theories in relation to alternative ones, whereas practitioners of pseudo science are oblivious to alternative theories.
4. Science uses simple theories that have broad explanatory power, whereas pseudo science uses theories that require many extra hypotheses for particular explanations.
5. Science progresses over time by developing new theories that explain newly discovered facts, whereas pseudo science is stagnant in doctrine and applications.[30]

The idea that similar objects exert influence on each other assumes "deeper" metaphysical similitude. To quote Sal Restivo who wrote critically of Fritjof Capra's *Tao of Physics*, "the basic assumption is that if

---

30 Thagard, 2010, p. 27.

the imagery and metaphoric content between physics and mysticism is similar, the conceptual content must be similar and the experience of reality must also be similar among particle physicists and eastern mystics."[31] Superficial similarities begin to take on extra weight. First a metaphysical equivalence is established. If two entities evoke similar subjective experience and imagery, resemblance thinking leads one to conclude that they *must* be about the same reality: thus the dance of Shiva becomes another way to describe the result from a cloud chamber. Once such connections are made, it is easy to see how the epistemological status of a cloud-chamber and particle physics gets transferred to Eastern spiritualism, or how (as we see, below), a Vivekananda can turn a yogi in meditation into a counterpart of a scientist in a lab. This kind of *status-transfer through resemblances* creates pseudo science, which is nothing more than ideas pretending to be scientific without actually undergoing the tests for empirical verification.

Social scientific interest in the harm "resemblance thinking" can do was given a fresh boost recently by Daniel Kahneman's popular book, *Thinking Slow, Thinking Fast* in which he recounts a well-known experiment he did in the 1970s. Without going into the experimental details which will take us too far afield, this is what he and his co-researcher (Amos Tversky) found:[32] when people make analogies with a cultural stereotype, they always end up making wrong guesses at probability. Kahneman considers "representativeness heuristic" to be one of the major sources of cognitive illusions that are found among otherwise normal people. The term "heuristic" here stands for judgmental short-cuts that provide quick, intuitive answers to questions that puzzle us.[33]

---

31 Restivo 1978, p. 151.

32 Amos Tversky, a psychologist, worked with Kahneman for many years. He passed away in 1996 and the Nobel Prize for their work was awarded to Kahneman alone in 2002. Kahneman belongs to the select group of non-economists who have won the Nobel Prize in economics.

33 These intuitive jumps at answers are what constitute the "thinking fast" in Kahneman's book *Thinking, Fast and Slow.* The fast-paced component of the process of thinking is referred to as the System 1, while the slow, more deliberative, effort-full component is referred to as the System 2. Kahneman's and Tversky's work stands out for their experimental exploration of the System 1. The intuitive System 1 operates through associative thinking, based upon superficial similarities which can provide quick answers to questions that are quite complex. But the price for

The representativeness heuristic works through resemblance thinking pretty much as described by Thagard and Restivo (see above). A clear exposition of what this heuristic involves goes as follows:

> The representativeness heuristic involves a reflexive tendency to assess the similarity of objects and events along salient dimensions and to organize them on the basis of one overarching rule: "Like goes with like." Among other things, the representativeness heuristic reflects the belief that *a member of a given category ought to resemble the category prototype* and that *an effect ought to resemble the cause that produced it.*[34]

What is the significance of "resemblance thinking" for the task at hand, namely, how *Yoga Sūtra*s were re-written in the vocabulary of science? As I show below, the seemingly scientific description of modern yoga meets all the features of pseudo science discussed in this section: it is steeped in resemblance thinking, its practitioners are dogmatic and not bothered by the lack of independent evidence or with obvious contradictions with accepted science; and for all its claims of being a "science", it has made no contribution to any real science.

6. Resemblance thinking in the Western and Indic traditions

In order to fully understand how yoga got scientized, it is important to add a historical dimension to resemblance thinking. Simply put, re-

---

"thinking fast" is that more often than not, our intuitive answers are wrong and misleading. That is why rationality, according to Kahneman, is not intelligence that can be measured through IQ tests, but rather consists of "thinking slow", of engaging the System 2 with the data provided by System 1.

34 Gilovich and Savitsky, 1996. The authors give many examples of how pseudo science is generated through this style of thinking. One particularly striking example comes from the discovery by Barry Marshall and Robin Warren of Australia that stomach ulcers are caused by a bacterium and not by stress alone. (The two were awarded the 2005 Nobel Prize in medicine for this discovery). The medical community initially ridiculed the idea as preposterous, because the belief that stress was the real cause of peptic ulcers was too strongly entrenched. But the stress-ulcer connection was based upon nothing more than an intuitive association between the two: "Because the burning feeling of an ulcerated stomach was similar to the gut-wrenching, stomach-churning feeling of extreme stress, albeit more severe, the connection seemed natural." This is nothing but "like goes with like" style of thinking: *effects* (symptoms) which feel alike are assumed to be brought about by the same/similar/like *causes*. One can see how this style of thinking leads to ideas about causation which *seem* correct and "scientific", but are actually false.

semblance thinking as described in the previous section, constituted the dominant episteme of ancient civilizations right through the Middle Ages upto the Early Modern era. To use Foucault's vocabulary, a chain of "similitudes" between the heavens above and earthly affairs below constituted the "positive unconscious of knowledge" that does not register in the consciousness of the scientist, but is nevertheless very much there.[35]

Before the Scientific Revolution that unfolded from the 16th through the 18th century, humanity everywhere lived in a magical world in which all that happened in the heavens above (the macrocosm), was reflected in the earthly life of humans below (the microcosm). Or to put it simply, "as above, so below". Figuring out the hidden resemblances, or correspondences, between the macrocosm and the microcosm was considered the highest form of wisdom: what were the stars trying to tell us about human affairs? How are the signs of God's meaning and purpose imprinted on the shapes, sizes and textures of plants, animal and even stones and minerals? How is the macrocosm contained in the microcosm of human body? This knowledge of correspondences was to be found both by observing signs of similitude between above and below, but it was to be confirmed by turning inwards, by feeling the indwelling god in your soul. The knowledge of hidden ("occult") resemblances was highly valued, as it allowed *manipulation of the unobservable entities and powers in the heavens by manipulating their known counterparts*: this was the source of the powers attributed to prayer, rituals, talismans, magical incantations etc. Clearly, the correspondence relations were supposed to work as resemblance relations as understood above: like

---

35 "Up to the end of the sixteenth century resemblances played a constructive role in the knowledge of the Western culture. It was resemblances that largely guided exegesis and interpretation of texts; it was resemblances that organized the play of symbols; made possible knowledge of things visible and invisible and controlled the art of representing them. The universe was folded upon itself: the earth echoing the sky, faces seeing themselves reflected in the stars, and plants holding in their stems secrets that were useful to man." Michel Foucault, 1970, p. 17. To this one can only add that similitudes constituted the main style of thinking in non-Western cultures, especially the cultures of Asia, as well.

goes with like, similar effects had similar causes, and in controlling one can control the other.[36]

Thinking through similitudes or correspondences between macro and microcosm flourished in the neo-Platonic academy founded in Florence by Cosimo De Medici in the second half of the 15h century where Marsillo Ficino translated into Latin a newly discovered Greek manuscript *Corpus Hermeticum* (supposedly), originating with semi-divine Hermes, and dating back to the time of Moses. This was considered at that time to be the most ancient expression of "primordial wisdom" or "Eternal Truth" that predated Christianity. This "Hermetical" or "esoteric" tradition differed from Judeo-Christian tradition in imagining a spiritual force emanating from a divine mind to animate the material world. This created a state of discord with the Christian teachings which opposed any attempt to assign meanings and purposes to material nature, as it would take away from God's omnipotence. Esotericism in the West, therefore, has always existed at some tension with the Bible, even though elements of it were absorbed into the Christian tradition as well.[37]

It is in the Indic/Eastern religions where correspondence-thinking really comes into its own. In the Vedic tradition, the correspondences are to be established not between two, but between three planes of existence: "the macro-cosmos, or *adhidevta*, the sphere of gods; the meso-cosmos or the ritual sphere, *adhijajan*, related to the sacrifice or the yagna; and the micro-cosmos, *adhyatama*, relating to the self. … entities, things, forces, activities … [on all three planes are supposed to] have essential affinities to related others."[38] Clearly, the concern of the Vedic thinkers was to discover the connections that bind the three spheres to each other. The underlying assumption was that the cosmos is a web of relationships and things that merely *appear* to stand alone, are *actually*

---

36 The Western esoteric tradition had four necessary features: correspondence thinking, vitalism (i.e., seeing nature as alive), imagination and mediation and personal experience of transmutation (Hanegraaff 1998, pp. 396-401). For similarities between the Western esoteric tradition and Hinduism, see De Michelis 2005, pp. 27-31.

37 Nicholas Goodrick-Clarke (2009) is a good source for history of western occult.

38 Smith 1998, pp. 46-47.

connected. These connections are not visible to ordinary people, but accessible only to those with philosophical and ritual knowledge.

Indeed, as the noted scholar of the Vedic tradition Brian Smith has observed, finding resemblances between the three spheres constitutes the "philosophical center around which all Vedic thought revolves" and the surfeit of analogies between otherwise dissimilar things is not a symptom of over-active imagination of ancient Vedic priests, but rather the very basis of Vedic rituals.[39] That correspondence-thinking is basic to Indic thought is evident from the fact that the literal meaning of "Upanishad", is simply "connection" or "equivalence".[40] Indeed, the deepest spiritual truth of the identity of the individual *atman* with Brahman, or the World Soul was arrived at by drawing parallels between the two: just as the human body is supposed to have a soul that is eternal, so was the universe ensouled.[41] Analogical thinking is not limited to the orthodox Vedic texts and rituals, but continues to serve as the basis of astrology and allied divination methods which are widely practiced in India. Indeed, it is fair to say with Axel Michaels that "establishment of identity by equating it with something else" has become the dominant "identificatory habitus" of modern India which allows Indians to accept different, even contradictory ideas, as "all the same".[42]

Brahman, the World Soul that is present as potency in every particle of the universe, serves as the metaphysical nexus of all connec-

---

39 Smith, p. 47. The most well-known example of analogical thinking is the opening paragraph of the *Bṛhadāraṇyaka Upanishad* in which the body of a sacrificial horse is analogized with the cosmos: "The head of the sacrificial horse, clearly, is the dawn – its sight is the sun, its breath the wind and its gaping mouth the fire common to all men. The body of the sacrificial horse is the year – its back is the sky, its abdomen is the intermediate region and the underbelly the earth.... When it yawns, lightning flashes, when it shakes itself, it thunders and when it urinates, it rains.... its neighing is speech itself." See Olivelle,1996, p. 7.

40 Olivelle, 1996, p. Iii.

41 Other examples: the 'Puruṣa-Sūkta' of *Ṛg Veda* where parts of the universe are described as parts of *Puruṣa*, or a giant man; and the funeral hymn addresses the departed: "'Let thine eyes go to the sun, thy breath to the wind.' When the Vedic sacrifice is interiorized, the body itself becomes a microcosm of the universe: the spinal cord becomes identified with Sumeru, the supposed *axis mundi* of the universe, the four limbs to be four continents, head to be the world of Devas, the two eyes to be the Sun and the Moon." Hiriyanna, 1993, p. 55.

42 Michaels, 2004, p. 7.

tions; while the Vedic ritual, or *yajna*, serves as the means for activating the potencies that lie within. Thus unlike the Abrahamic religions in which the divine is separate from matter, the Vedic tradition provides a complete metaphysics to make rational sense of resemblance relations, along with a highly developed ritual technology to manipulate the causal effects of resemblances. The Vedic ritual, as is well known, gradually got interiorized and took the form of a mystical union of the self within with the universal soul.

7. The *fin de siècle* America: Growth of the "Cultic Milieu"

As we know, Vivekananda grew up in the midst of a great ferment of ideas about science, religion, philosophy, nationalism that marked the Hindu Renaissance, especially in the second half of the 19th century and especially in his native Bengal. We also know that he arrived in the United States of America in 1893, 30-years-old, first time in the Western world, determined to speak up for his faith and his country, both of which had long suffered the condescension of British colonists and missionaries. He spent four crucial years lecturing and networking in the US.

In order to understand the kind of paradigm-defining innovations that Vivekananda brought to Hinduism it is important to understand his cultural context – which includes *both* India and the United States. Given the objective of this essay – that is, to understand how Vivekananda scientized meditational yoga – his familiarity with the crisscrossing intellectual currents in the two sites has obvious relevance. What follows in the rest of this section (and the next) is a somewhat unusually detailed examination of the intellectual milieu in America (this section) and in India (the next section).[43] Those readers who are in a hurry to get to how Patanjali's *sūtras* were scientized can skip these sections without losing the thread of the argument.

Thanks to Elizabeth de Michelis' *History of Modern Yoga*, it is now well established that Vivekananda literally stepped off the boat into the "cultic milieu" that was thriving in New York, Boston and other indus-

---

43 The material for these two sections is largely taken from an earlier essay of mine. See Nanda, 2010.

trial cities on the Eastern seaboard which had, to use de Michelis' words, "a proto-Woodstock feel". [44] Rapid industrialization had brought with it ideas of progress and individualism that fuelled a revolt against Calvinist ideas of sinfulness of man and the need for God's grace for salvation. Moreover, the bloody civil war had claimed countless lives, and people grieving for their loved ones were seeking solace in spiritualism which promised communication with the dead. As a result, there was a flowering of alternative religions including spiritualism, Swedenborgianism,[45] Mesmerism, Christian Science, Theosophy, mind-reading, astrology, psychic research and other more *avant garde* alternatives (Transcendentalism of the "Boston Brahmins" Emerson, Walt Whitman and the Unitarians). What was common to all these movements was a belief – originally derived from neo-Platonic and esoteric Western philosophies and later supplemented with Hindu teachings – in a spiritual substance, or "mind-stuff" that permeated the entire cosmos, connecting the human soul with the soul of everything else. This spiritual substance was variously understood as a magnetic fluid (as in Mesmerism), as simply Holy Spirit in Swedenborgianism and Christian Science, or "*prāṇa* " or "energy" or "ether" as in Theosophy (and eventually, also in Vivekananda's writings).

Out of all these new religious movements, theosophy as taught by the Theosophical Society is most relevant for a proper understanding of

---

44 See de Michelis for the Woodstock comparison, p. 114. Cultic milieu, as defined by Colin Campbell in 1972, is the "cultural underground" of a society and includes all those groups and individuals who find the conventional belief systems of their time and place as inadequate and unsatisfactory. As a result, they seek out beliefs and indulge in practices that are "heterodox or deviant in relation to the dominant cultural orthodoxies". p. 122.

45 The possible connection with Brahmo Samaj is examined in the next section. Emmanuel Swedenborg (1688-1772) was a well respected scientist who worked with the Swedish Board of Mines and did significant work in metallurgy and mining engineering. Hanegraaff (1998, p. 424) suggests that his scientific work led him to give up on finding any signs of the divine in nature. This intellectual crisis was resolved by a vision of Christ which he interpreted as a divine command to explain the spiritual meaning of the Bible to people. He devised an elaborate system of correspondences by which he explained the natural world as a mirror that reflects the spiritual world.

the emergence of scientism in neo-Hinduism.[46] The Theosophical Society's importance lies in its borrowings from Hindu doctrines, its physical presence in India and the active role it played in the Hindu Renaissance and the struggle for independence. But to fully understand where Theosophists were coming from, we have to get to know the 19th century "cultic milieu" in the US.

As mentioned earlier, the late 19th century America had a Woodstock-like feel about it, with a variety of proto-New Age movements thriving in the big cities, especially in the Northeast. These movements had broken free from the mainstream Protestant Christianity and sought an alternative form of religious experience.

Participation in these movements was by no means a fringe phenomenon. Bruce Campbell estimates that at its height around 1855, the spiritualist movement alone claimed between one to two million adherents. Given that the total population of the US at that time was about 25

---

46 The Theosophical Society was founded in New York City in November 1875 by a Russian émigré Helena Petrovna Blavatsky (1831-1891), and her American friend and "spiritual twin" Henry Steel Olcott (1832-1907). "HPB" as she was sometimes called, was a woman with a colorful past involving psychic phenomena, magical materializations including mysterious letters from Tibetan Masters or "mahatmas" and an intense involvement in a range of secret societies including Rosicrucian Freemasonry in her native Russia, Masonic lodges, Sufis and Oriental secret societies in the Middle East and Europe.

After her endless travels, HPB arrived in New York in 1873. Almost immediately, she began work on her first major book, *The Isis Unveiled: A Master Key to the Mysteries of Ancient and Modern Science and Theology*, which appeared in print in 1877. In the meantime, she and Olcott established the Theosophical Society with three aims: to promote brotherhood of man, to encourage a comparative study of ancient and modern religions, philosophies and sciences, and to carry out "scientific" investigations of unexplained laws of nature involving hidden psychic powers immanent in matter.

The founders soon set sail for India, arriving in Bombay in February 1879. By 1882, they had established the headquarters of their society in Adyar in the state of Madras (now Tamil Nadu), where it stands even today. After some initial misunderstandings with the Indian organization that they had affiliated themselves with – Arya Samaj founded by Swami Dayananda Saraswati (1824-1882) – Theosophical Society soon emerged as an all-India organization that brought the western educated Indian elite into close contact with liberal members of the British community, including figures like A.P. Sinnett and Allan Octavian Hume, who later went on to form the Indian National Congress in 1885. See Nanda, 2010.

million, the level of participation in spiritualism was quite significant.[47] What is more, most of these movements were a popular rather than an elite phenomenon: they involved ordinary Americans "from 'thinking persons' on down to the level of shopkeepers and dressmakers [in Boston] who took it for granted that 'psychic force' was a reality while the language of mind-cure could be heard in everyday conversations."[48] According to Stephen Prothero, "spiritualists were a diverse lot... including women, blacks, urban and rural laborers, southerners, and Catholics", who were drawn to the populist impulse of spiritualism which "criticized the privileged knowledge of the clergy and appealed to the natural wisdom of unlettered folk".[49]

The growth of the cultic milieu was part of a historical trend in the West where, as Nicholas Goodrick-Clarke points out, "esoteric ideas attend the breakdown of settled religious orthodoxies and socioeconomic orders."[50] Rapid rise in levels of industrialization and rising levels of prosperity had brought with them new ideas of progress, free will and efficacy of individual effort which were fuelling a revolt against Calvinism:

> ...progress in science and technology fostered confidence in human reason and gave credence to belief in progress. These developments challenged an understanding of man which emphasized sinfulness and depravity, the control of God, the need for grace, and preoccupation with the hereafter.[51]

But the revolt against conventional pieties of Protestant Christianity did not mean secularization. Instead there was a deep crisis of faith affecting growing numbers of thoughtful people who were dissatisfied, in equal measure, with Christian orthodoxy and the mainstream materialistic science of that era. As a result, they could neither pray to the personal God of their Christian faith, nor accept the bleak mechanical philosophy of Newtonian science. Those attracted to the cultic milieu were looking for "a reasonable alternative to what they saw as the 'irrational dogma' of Christianity on the one hand, and the 'dogmatic ra-

---

47 Bruce Campbell, 1980, p. 16.
48 de Michelis 2004, pp. 113-114).
49 Prothero, 1993, p. 199.
50 Nicholas Goodrick-Clarke, 2008, p. 13.
51 Campbell 1980, p. 17.

tionality' of the Enlightenment, on the other."[52] It was in this context that the alternative forms of religiosity, which would later embrace modern interpretations of Hinduism and Buddhism, were gaining ground. Three features of the cultic milieu in the *fin de siècle* America are relevant to our story.

One, the cultic milieu had high regard for Wise Men from the East. At a time when working men from India and China were objects of discrimination, and the country was rife with moral panic over "tide of turbans" and the "Yellow peril", gurus and spiritual teachers found America to be a very hospitable milieu. As an Indian immigrant, Saint (sant) Nihal Singh, wrote in an essay that appeared in Los Angeles' *Out West* in 1909:

> East-Indian religious teachers and students have received better treatment than Hindoo[sic] laborers. Of all men from India who have visited the US, the late Swami Vivekananda stands pre-eminent. He seems to have won an instant way into the heart of American men and women of highest intellect and culture. ... There is a mystical charm attached to the Hindoo fortune teller. It is sufficient that he comes from the East. It must follow that he is a "Wise Man".[53]

This sentiment was echoed by another Indian immigrant, Krishnal-al Shridharan who wrote in his autobiography, *My India, My America* that Indian "Wise Men" could be found among the "ten or twenty Indians who have some claim to upper-bracket earnings in the US. One or two of these priests have real-estate interests in some of the most fashionable purlieus of NY, Boston and LA and some are millionaires. India is over-advertised with respect to her religiosity...."[54]

Secondly, the cultic milieu was fluid. Those seeking different modes of religiosity moved in and out of a range of religious movements which sometimes shared nothing more than a rejection of Trinitarian Christianity. Crossovers from Unitarianism to Free Thought and from there to spiritualism, Theosophy, Buddhism and Vedanta were common. Henry Steel Olcott himself moved from his Presbyterian beginnings to spiritualism to Theosophy and esoteric Buddhism, while Annie Besant shed

---

52 Hanegraaff 1998, p. 414.
53 Quoted here from Tweed and Prothero, 1999, p. 85.
54 Shridharan 1941, pp. 98-99.

her Protestant upbringing first for freethinking and socialism and then for Theosophy.

Most Americans who came to Asian religions "were women, many were foreign born, and a good number came to Hinduism (and Buddhism) out of alternative religious traditions, such as Theosophy, New Thought and Christian Science."[55] One of Swami Vivekananda's devout followers, Sister Christine (born Christine Greenstidel), who migrated to America from Germany in 1869 when she was three years old, was a Catholic who practiced Christian Science. She became a nun in the Ramakrishna mission after she listened to a lecture by Swami Vivekananda in a Unitarian Church in 1894. She later moved to Bengal where she co-founded the Sister Nivedita Girls' School. To take another example, Marie Canavarro (1849-1933), or Sister Sanghamitra, was the second American to take Buddhist vows on the US soil. She did that in New York City in the presence of Anagarika Dharmapala, the Buddhist monk from Sri Lanka. Her spiritual journey took her from Catholicism to Theosophy, to Buddhism, to Bahai faith, to Hinduism. By the time she wrote her autobiography, *Insight into the Far East* in 1925, she had embraced Vedanta at Swami Paramananda's Ananda Ashram in California.[56] Asian religions were thus thoroughly integrated into the American cultic milieu which made it possible for ideas, personalities and organized movements to move effortlessly in both directions.

Thirdly, and finally, the cultic milieu was scientistic in the sense described in an earlier section. Even though rejection of materialism of modern science fuelled the growth of the cultic milieu, such was the hegemony of science that even the most heterodox religious-spiritual movements felt compelled to show that, at a minimum, their faith rested on rational foundations and was not contrary to the experimental spirit of modern science.

This tension between hostility to the materialism of modern science on the one hand, and yet, the imperative to speak in its language was resolved by two strategies. On the practical level, it meant practicing and investigating the occult in a "scientific" way. Thus mesmerists went about conducting experiments, phrenologists measured the

55   Tweed and Prothero, p. 145.
56   Both examples come from Tweed and Prothero, 1999.

human head while spiritualists kept careful records of séances. On the more theoretical level, however, spiritualism and allied psychic practices failed to make much headway. Communication with spirits of dead people, or manipulation of animal magnetism or psychic energy provided "evidence" for belief in immortal soul, but the spiritualists could not explain the nature of this soul, nor relate their idea of the soul to any known tradition that wouldn't lead them back to the dogmas of Christianity.

This is where the Theosophical Society came in: it provided an ancient and yet seemingly "scientific" tradition for explaining the spiritualist phenomena. While the more elite counter-cultural movements of Transcendentalists and Unitarians tended to stay away from scholastic debates about metaphysics and doctrine, Theosophical Society reveled in metaphysics. It linked spiritualist beliefs and practices to an amalgam of ancient cosmological doctrines with roots in Hermetic and Renaissance neo-Platonism, updated with the Orientalist discovery of India on the one hand, and with the Darwinian theory of evolution on the other.[57] As Goodrick-Clarke sums it up:

> In the West, Theosophy was perhaps the single most important factor in the modern occult revival. It redirected the fashionable interest in spiritualism towards a coherent doctrine combining cosmology, modern anthropology and the theory of evolution with man's spiritual development. It drew upon the traditional sources of Western esotericism, globalizing them through restatement in terms of Asian religions, with which the West had come into colonial contact.[58]

The key to this synthesis of Western esotericism, Asian religions, evolutionary theory and laws of physics lay in conceiving God as a creative force that acts as a *vital force that is internal to nature*, and not

---

57 Stephen Prothero sees the Theosophical Society's attempt to provide theoretical foundation for spiritualism as "an elite attempt to reform spiritualism from above. If spiritualism constituted a democratic or populist movement in the history of American religion, then early theosophy represented an attempt by elites like Blavatsky and Olcott to reform spiritualism by "uplifting" its masses out of their supposed philosophical and moral vulgarities, to transform masses of ghost-seeking spiritualists into theorists of the astral planes" (1993, p. 198). Ordinary "ghost-seeking spiritualists" did not take kindly to Theosophical Society, advising them to pack up and move to the Orient!

58 Goodrick-Clarke, 2004, p. 18.

externally as a Designer. If divine agency could be imagined as an invisible, hidden (or occult) "energy" that enlivens matter, then it could presumably be studied as scientifically as any other form of energy, or any other element of nature (molecules, radiations and particles) that is invisible to the human eye. This paradigm of ensouled nature had the obvious advantage of explaining magic, paranormal and other occult phenomena as being internal to nature and therefore amenable to experiential testing, albeit using "super-physical" modes of "seeing" in the mind's eye, rather than through the physical eye. As Blavatsky famously put it, "Magic is but a science, a profound knowledge of the Occult forces in Nature, and of laws governing the visible and invisible world." Theosophists saw themselves not as mystics, or as naïve spiritualists communing with the spirits of dead people. They saw themselves as, in Henry Olcott's words, scientists who were seeking a "science dealing with strictly verifiable order of facts, though an order transcending that with which physical science is concerned."[59]

Indeed, what they meant by "science" came out very clearly when Theosophists tried to defend themselves against critics who accused them of trying to convert Indians to a foreign religion or to a new sect. Henry Olcott liked to remind his Indian audiences that they had come to India not to convert them to some new Western cult, but only to save them from the ills of materialism and skepticism on the one hand, and the false religion of Christianity that the missionaries were trying to spread. In a lecture delivered in the town hall of Calcutta in 1882, Olcott assured his Bengali audience:

> We are not preaching a new religion, or founding a new sect, or a new school of philosophy or occult science. The Hindu *Sastras*, the Buddhist *Gathas* and the Zoroastrian *Desatri* contain every essential idea that we have ever propounded, and our constant theme has been that Theosophy is the scientific and the only firm basis of religion. We deny that there is the slightest conflict between true religion

---

59 Olcott, 1895, p. 23. This impulse to study the paranormal in a scientific spirit was not limited to Theosophists. John Gray (2011) shows how the great minds of that era, including Alfred Wallace (the co-discover of the theory of evolution by natural selection), William James the psychologist and some renowned experimental physicists, went about designing experiments that could confirm the existence of spirit that could survive death.

and true science. We deny that any religion *can* be true that does not rest upon scientific lines.[60]

The reference to Eastern texts was crucial to what "science" meant to Theosophists. They believed that a *holistic science which included the spiritual dimension of nature* was known to the ancients before Judeo-Christian monotheism overpowered it. The original home of this ancient wisdom had been a subject of intense debate and controversy. The Western esoteric tradition had long considered pre-Hellenic and Hellenized Egypt – the home of the "thrice great" Hermes Trismegistus and the great Neo-Platonist philosopher Plotinus (205-270 A.D.) who taught in Alexandria – as the original home of the ancient wisdom.[61] But by the time Theosophy arrived in the 19th century cultic milieu, India and the Vedas had already begun to displace Egypt and the Corpus Hermeticum. In her first major book, *Isis Unveiled*, Blavatsky declared Hinduism to be the original source of primordial wisdom out of which all other religions and sciences had emerged. Most of her understanding of Hinduism was derived from the writings of Louis Jacolliot (1837-1890) the French occultist and Indophile whose fanciful and unreliable writings on India – including his translation of the *Laws of Manu* – were extremely popular among the reading public and intellectuals in the late 19th century in the West. Madame Blavatsky apparently owned all 13 volumes of Jacolliot's India writings and made more than 50 references to him in her *Isis Unveiled*. India and Hindu doctrines of *karma*, reincarnation and the seven-fold nature of human beings became central to her mature work, *The Secret Doctrine*.[62]

One can safely say that Theosophy, among all other esoteric movements in the West, moved closest to India and embraced the doctrines of Hinduism.

---

60 Olcott, 1895, p. 145.
61 The writings of Hermes Trismegistus were rediscovered and translated into Latin by the Florentine humanist, Marsilio Ficino in 1463 under the patronage of Cosimo de Medici, the leading merchant-prince of Florence. Ficino was also responsible for reviving Neo-Platonism.
62 David Smith, 2004. It appears that Nietzsche derived his understanding of Hinduism from Jacolliot's *Manu*, a book he seems to have read with great attention. See David Smith (2004).

8. The *Fin de Siècle* India: Crisis of faith and co-option of science

By the waning decades of the 19th century, a new generation of educated, urban and urbane Indian elites had emerged, especially in Bengal, the cultural heart of colonial India. They have been described as
"the Oriental version of the Enlightenment man".[63] Like their Western
counterparts, these men were restless: not altogether religious and not
altogether secular, they stood at the cusp of faith and skepticism. They
simultaneously felt the need to defend the tradition of their forefathers,
especially against the colonial critics, and at the same time, felt a compulsion to modernize and reform the religious tradition they were born
into. While they expressed a great faith in science and reason, they
shied away from secular humanism.

They had inherited a crisscrossing stream of ideas. On the one
hand, they had absorbed the myth of the Hindu Golden Age created
by the British and German Orientalists. On the other hand, they were
exposed to modern ideas and ways of thinking through Christian and
Hindu educational institutions that had sprung up in Calcutta and other
urban centers. In addition, they were painfully aware of the low opinion
many Christian missionaries and colonial administrators had of their
Hindu faith, rituals and culture. They were caught in pretty much the
same dilemma as their counterparts in the West: *they could neither pray
to the God(s) of their fathers and forefathers, but nor were they fully comfortable with the stark materialism of modern science which came with
colonial baggage, to boot.* Thus they faced the same old quandary that
had haunted the post-Enlightenment generation in the West, namely,
how to harmonize science and religion, or modern ideas with tradition.

This shared crisis of faith served as a "link between the enlightened
few in Calcutta and the enlightened few in England and the United
States".[64] The *first generation* of this link was undoubtedly the heroic
age of British Orientalism which had lasted from 1773 to 1837. After
the British Orientalism came to an end, a *second generation* of the "re-

---

63 De Michelis, 2004, p. 52. All the major public figures of Bengal Renaissance were
    men. But Swami Vivekananda and Sri Aurobindo had Western-born female devo-
    tees/companions – Sister Nivedita and the Mother, respectively – who emerged as
    well-respected public figures in their own right.

64 Kopf, 1979, p. 4.

ligious left" that was rebelling against the dogmas of Calvinist Christianity in their native lands – including those like Unitarians who were still at least nominally Christian and those like Freemasons and Theosophists who espoused esoteric and occult beliefs – began to arrive on the shores of India from Britain and the United States. These religious skeptics and seekers were led to India in part by the scholarly output of the Orientalists which had introduced them to Hindu *Vedas*, *Bhagavad Gita*, *Manusmriti*, *Vishnu Purana* and other sacred books. As described earlier, they were seeking a rational theology cleansed of revealed dogmas of Christianity.

In the post-Orientalist period, especially after the 1857 rebellion when the British began to aggressively promote Westernization, it was this second generation that filled in the gap left behind by the Orientalists. As Elizabeth de Michelis points out,

> the only body of interlocutors that was now [i.e., after the thwarting of Orientalist plans for Anglo-Indian cooperation] eager to communicate and cooperate with Indians qua Indians was that of the esotericists, whether Christian [Unitarians] or otherwise. Bengalis reciprocated, while Orient-inspired Romantic, Transcendentalist, occultist and in due course theosophical ideas were being propagated by a steadily growing body of literature, or through lecture tours and personal contacts.[65]

Providing more evidence for Jocelyn Godwin's well-known thesis that "Blavatsky's Theosophy owed as much to the skeptical Enlightenment ...as it did to the concept of spiritual enlightenment with which it is more readily associated",[66] it was the Unitarians, who shared the Enlightenment skepticism against Trinitarian Christianity, who prepared the ground for acceptance of Theosophical ideas in India. The early decades saw the emergence of neo-Vedantic Enlightenment, which gradually embraced more spiritualist and esoteric ideas.

The contact between Boston, London and Calcutta began with Raja Rammohan Roy's (1774-1833) attempt to interpret the Vedas and the Upanishads to bring them in accord with monotheism strongly influenced by Unitarian ideas that were emerging from William Channing and Joseph Tuckerman from Boston, Reverend Lant Carpenter in

---

65 De Michelis, 2004, p. 47.
66 Godwin, 1994, p. xi.

Britain and other Christians with Unitarian leanings in Bengal itself. Roy absorbed the rational theology of Unitarians that eschewed revelation and depended more upon intuition and personal experience of the divine and tried to find it in the Vedas and Upanishads. In his many debates with his Christian friends and critics, he tried to "prove that the message of the Vedanta not only contained the unity of God, but did so in a way superior to the Judeo-Christian Bible... because it did not attempt to categorize the attributes of the Almighty – a gesture that Rammohan found both anthropomorphic and futile. *Rammohan was now using Unitarianism in an Indian way...*"[67] This view of the divine became the basis of Brahmo Samaj he founded in Calcutta in 1828 which took a lead in combating socially regressive practices like child marriage and widow immolation.

The next step toward spiritualism was taken by Debendranath Tagore (1817-1905), who took on the leadership of Brahmo Samaj after Roy's death. While Roy had tried to reconcile his Unitarian faith in One God with the Vedas, Tagore broke free of this compulsion to refer back to the Vedas or any holy book. After a deep and long study of Hindu scriptures, he felt he could not accept the doctrine of *karma* and rebirth. Consequently, he made a break and announced that not the Vedas, but "the pure, unsophisticated heart was the seat of Brahmoism" and henceforth Brahmos "could accept those texts only which accorded with that heart. Those sayings that disagreed with the heart [they] could not accept."[68] Under his leadership, Brahmo Samaj gave up the idea of the infallibility of the Vedas and instead made the truth of the Vedas dependent upon the spiritual experiences of believers. This idea was to play an important role in the later development of self-understanding of modern Hinduism both as a "religion of science" in which spiritual experience began to serve as the basis of empiricism, and Hindus as a people endowed with the "yoga faculty". But at the time when Brahmo Samaj first adopted this principle, it was literally unprecedented as "there is simply no evidence of an indigenous Indian counterpart to the rhetoric of experience prior to the colonial period".[69]

---

67 Kopf, 1979, p. 13, emphasis added.
68 Quoted here from de Michelis 2004, p. 59.
69 Sharf, 1998, p. 100.

The real turn toward spiritual scientism took place with Keshub Chunder Sen's famous "New Dispensation" which laid the foundation for Swami Vivekananda's paradigm defining writings and teachings.[70] Keshub Chunder Sen (1838-1884) was a protégé of Debendranath Sen, but he later split from the original Brahmo Samaj in 1866 to start his own Brahmo Samaj (leaving the original body to attach the prefix "Adi", or the Original, to its name). For most of his life, he remained staunchly committed to the Unitarian social gospel and counted the American Unitarian minister Charles Dall to be an honorary Brahmo. But by all accounts, he underwent a profound change in the years immediately following a trip to England in 1870. He apparently came back from England convinced that:

> the Christian vision needed completion by a distinctively Indian contribution, and implementation by an Indian....thus was born the idea of New Dispensation, an amalgam of ideas and practices culled from different religions, especially Hinduism and Christianity, with Keshub, the Great Man, at the head.[71]

He formally declared the formation of the Church of New Dispensation (or Nava Vidhan) in 1879 with an express purpose of bringing about such a completion. His "church" sought to harmonize all religions; harmonize all religions with science; and to provide empirical evidence for such a concordance. As he announced rather grandly in 1880: "We are going to enter into *a new domain of a new dispensation, that of science and faith harmonized. ... In the new faith everything is scientific.* In all your beliefs and in all your prayers, faith and reason shall be harmonized in a true science."[72]

Keshub found an ideal exemplar of his Nava Vidhan in Ramakrishna Parmahansa (1836-1886), a tantric worshipper of Goddess Kali in a Calcutta temple, who he met in 1875 and who he thought could *demonstrate,* through personal experience which could be repeated by others, the harmony of all religions. Ramakrishna was an intensely spiritual man who spent his entire life seeking direct experience of God:

---

70 Elizabeth de Michelis places Sen somewhere in-between "Debendranath Tagore's neo-Vedantic romanticism and Swami Vivekananda's neo-Vedantic occultism", with Sen progressing throughout his life from the former toward the latter (p. 74).
71 Julius Lipner, quoted from Brown, 2007, p. 431.
72 Brown 2007, p. 431. Emphasis added.

he taught that a "feeling for God" – directly seeing God and hearing God – were superior to book-learning which he compared to "mere dirt and straw after realization of God".[73] A worshipper of Kali, he "experimented" with Islam and Christianity by worshipping as a Muslim or a Christian would do, observing all the rites and rituals of these faiths. From these experiences, he concluded that all religions lead to the same goal, namely, god realization, and therefore all are true.[74]

Keshub interpreted Ramakrishna's teachings as proof that religious harmony can be empirically demonstrated. This became his basis for asserting the "scientific" basis of New Dispensation and led him to invent highly syncretic rituals which combined, for example, traditional Vaishnava bhakti with Salvation Army-style parades and bands, Christian-style baptism ceremonies and "pilgrimages" in which he encouraged devotees to imaginatively replicate the spiritual experiences of Socrates, Moses, Mohammad, and Chaitanya, and so on.[75]

But even though he taught equal truth of all religions, he clearly singled out Hinduism as being more open to experiential knowledge of God because, as he wrote to Max Muller, he, as a Hindu was "free of biases of the true believer in a revealed religion".[76] Keshub can be counted among the architects of the idea of spirituality being the essence of Hinduism. Meticulous research by Elizabeth de Michelis shows that as he broke his ties with Unitarianism, he turned more and more to yoga and meditation, declaring "we Hindus are specially endowed with, and distinguished for, the yoga faculty, which is nothing but this power of spiritual communion and absorption. This faculty which we have inherited from our forefathers enables us to annihilate space and time...."[77]

73   Rambachan 1993, p. 33.

74   For a description of his experiments with god realization, see Farquhar, 1915, pp. 188-200. One of the lessons Ramakrishna drew from his belief that all religions are true was that religious conversions were pointless and that "every man should follow his own religion. A Christian should follow Christianity; a Mohammedan should follow Mohammedanism, and so on. For the Hindus, the ancient path, the path of the Aryan Rishis, is the best." p. 198.

75   Kopf, 1979, pp. 268-281.

76   Kopf, 1979, p. 270.

77   De Michelis, p. 89.

Thus Keshub initiated the process of braiding together mystical empiricism, scientific empiricism and Hindu exceptionalism in a potent mixture which has continued to beguile Hindu nationalists of all shades. This mixture was inherited by Swami Vivekananda, a protégé of both Keshub and Ramakrishna and through his enormous influence, it became the fundamental assumption of neo-Hinduism.[78]

This scientistic turn became most obvious in Keshub only close to his death in 1884. By that time, Madame Blavatsky had already published her first major book, *Isis Unveiled*, which came out in 1877. By 1879, Blavatsky and Olcott had already moved to India and were soon to establish the headquarters of their society in Adyar in Madras. By the time Keshub enunciated his New Dispensation in 1880, there were already "over a hundred branches of Theosophical Society in India and Hindus everywhere rejoiced in their work...Theosophy was providing a new defense of Hinduism for thousands of educated men, whose Western education had filled them with shivering doubts about their

---

78 It has been suggested by Elizabeth de Michelis and Mackenzie Brown recently that this concern with bringing about concordance of all religions with modern science was picked up by Keshub from his contact with the Swedenborg Society during his visit to London in 1870. Swedenborg Society shared the same intellectual space in the cultic milieu in the West as the Theosophical Society, Mesmerism, spiritualism and Transcendentalism. Its unique contribution was the application of scientific methods to the spiritual world, a project that Theosophical Society shared.

According to de Michelis (p.61), extensive contacts with Unitarians had already familiarized Sen and his fellow Brahmos to the Vedanta-influenced Transcendentalist writings of Emerson and Parker which had predisposed them favorably toward emphasizing spiritual experience over holy books and theological treatises as the basis of a universal religion. Thus Sen was receptive to the Swedenborgian and theosophical idea that spiritual experiences verify the spiritual phenomena in the same manner that sensory experiences verify the natural phenomena, and that the spiritual phenomena correspond with the natural world.

Mackenzie Brown (2007) provides more evidence. He quotes from the welcome speech at Swedenborg Society on June 2, 1870 when "New Dispensation" was mentioned as heralding "an astonishing revolution in modes of faith and forms of thought" following the passing away of old religions. Indeed, in the 19th century cultic milieu, the idea of "New Dispensation" was routinely used to refer to spiritualism and other occult movements. Brown suggests that this encounter made Sen receptive to the more metaphysical writings of the Theosophical Society.

religion."[79] Jocelyn Godwin has suggested that Blavatsky and Olcott originally intended to make contact with Brahmo Samaj, rather than with Arya Samaj.[80] Olcott himself admitted that he had "written to Keshub Babu to ask him to join us in our work, and I was ready to serve in any subordinate position, under and with anybody, no matter whom, in the interest of India and Indians." But, he goes on to say, "the back of the hand, not the palm, was offered to me."[81]Blavatsky had admired the founder of Brahmo Samaj, Raja Rammohan Roy as a great reformer, but she did not take kindly to the devaluation of the Vedas in favor of Unitarian Christianity among the post-Roy Brahmos. She also objected to Keshub's proclamations of himself as a prophet of the New Dispensation. It appears that Keshub returned the criticism, calling Blavatsky "an imposter", "adventurer" and a "pretender".[82] All this provides ample grounds to believe that Theosophical Society was not an unknown entity in India by the time Keshub took his neo-Vedantic-scientistic turn in the early 1880s. It is quite likely that Keshub was familiar with the content of Theosophical teachings, even though he disapproved of the famous "Theosophical twins" who had made India their home.

Theosophical Society was by no means the only organized body of esoteric thought that had found a niche in India. Freemasonry, which had the agenda of creating a universal brotherhood of Man in the One, had been present on the subcontinent since as far back as mid-18th century, brought to its shores by British aristocrats. Freemasons opened their doors to the "native gentlemen" in 1843, and by the early 1880s it had become a "fashion with the Indians to become members of the Freemasonry. Lawyers, judges and government officials were its members. Its membership gave a chance to mix with the high dignitaries and officials."[83] By 1920, there were 183 lodges in Calcutta (now Kolkata), Bombay (now Mumbai) and Madras (now Chennai).

One Bengali with one foot in Freemasonry and the other in Keshub's Brahmo Samaj was Narendranath Datta, the future Swami Vive-

---

79   Farquhar, 1915, p. 233.

80   Godwin, 1994, p. 320.

81   Olcott, 1895, p. 12.

82   Brown, 2007, p. 445, note 26.

83   Quoted from de Michelis, p. 69.

kananda. Vivekananda's spiritual and intellectual journey has been a topic of great scholarly interest. The outlines are clear: born in 1863 in Calcutta, he received the standard middle-class English medium education, and even joined the Freemasons as many aspiring young men of his milieu did in order to gain contacts among the elite. After initial sympathy with the socially more progressive wing of Brahmo Samaj, he became an active member of Keshub's wing (which had gradually turned its back on social reform) and joined the New Dispensation in 1880 when he was barely 19 years old. Even though he renounced his Brahmo affiliation later in life, he remained distrustful of revealed knowledge in favor of the kind of mystical empiricism and concordance of religions that the New Dispensation taught.

After Keshub's death in 1884, he came under the influence of Ramakrishna Parmahansa for pretty much the same reasons as Keshub: he saw Ramakrishna as providing empirical demonstration of God.[84] After Ramakrishna's death in 1886, leadership of his disciples fell upon Narendranath. But critical of the ecstatic devotionalism, anti-intellectualism and lack of social concerns among his brother monks, the future Vivekananda broke away and pursued his own quest. (He returned to establish the Ramakrishna Mission in Calcutta in 1897.) In 1893, he addressed the World Parliament of Religions in Chicago which made him a celebrity in the United States and back home in India.

It is through his deep engagement with the cultic milieu in the United States, where he stayed for other three-plus years after his Chicago address, that he began to blend neo-Vedantic esotericism and avant-garde American occultism. His years in America were spent discoursing – and raising money for his future work in India– in nu-

---

84 Young Narendranath was exposed to the writings of British empiricists, notably Locke, Berkeley and Hume in his college years and took to heart the empiricist dictum that all knowledge was dependent upon sense experience. This predisposed him toward Keshub's New Dispensation and even more fatefully, toward Ramakrishna's experiments with spiritualism. The often-told story has it that the first question he asked Ramakrishna when he went to see him at Dakshineshwar temple was "Sir, have you seen God?" to which Ramakrishna replied, "Yes, I see him just as I see you." The idea that direct experience of God is the most direct means of knowledge and therefore spiritualism is a kind of science remained one of the guiding principles of Vivekananda's philosophy. See, Emilsen (1984).

merous gatherings of Unitarians, Christian Scientists, Spiritualists, Swedenborgians, Transcendentalists and Theosophists who welcomed this celebrated Wise Man from the East. As he became familiar with the Western quest for a non-dogmatic spiritualism that was compatible with the Enlightenment values of scientific evidence, progress and evolution, he settled on Advaita Vedanta into which he read all that the Western seekers were seeking.

In the process, he created an image of his spiritual master, Ramakrishna – the devotee of Kali – as a great Vedantic sage who exemplified the rational, experiential and therefore "scientific" core of Advaita Vedanta. What is more, he claimed that this Advaita that he and his guru Ramakrishna taught, was the same doctrine taught by the great seventh century sage, Shankaracharya (788-820 CE). Thus he managed to read an experience-based way of knowing spiritual realities that eschewed doctrine and revelations back into the original teachings of Shankara.[85]

Where were the Theosophists in Vivekananda's journey? He did not have a good opinion of them and tried his best to dissuade his followers from joining them. Vivekananda's relationship with the founding members – especially with Olcott, Blavatsky having already left India for Europe by the time Vivekananda began to get involved in these issues in late 1880s – was fraught with mutual distrust, professional rivalry, and resentment against foreigners presuming to teach Hinduism to Hindus. William Emilsen has likened their relationship to that of porcupines huddling together who prick each other if they are too close, but yet, feel compelled to huddle because of the warmth they provide to each other. Vivekananda started out with a negative impression of Blavatsky and Olcott because of their prior dispute with Swami

---

85 But Shankara taught no such empiricism. If anything, he distrusted personal experience as a valid source of knowledge of the divine and insisted that Vedas themselves were the highest authority. According to Rambachan (1994, p. 3), "unlike Vivekananda, who presented the affirmation of *śruti* [the revealed scriptures, the Vedas] as having only a hypothetical or provisional validity and needing verification that only *anubhav* [experience] could provide, Shankara argued for *sruti* as the unique and self-valid source for our knowledge of absolute reality or Brahman. In relation to the gain of this knowledge, all ways of knowing were subordinate to *śruti*."

Dayananda, someone he held in great esteem. His negative impression deepened into a deep resentment when Olcott refused to recommend him for the World Parliament of Religions – a grudge he carried even after he emerged as a celebrity. (He managed to get to Chicago with the help of his old colleagues in the Brahmo Samaj). With his keen sense of which way the intellectual winds were blowing, moreover, Vivekananda came to the conclusion that Theosophists were a minority wing of the spiritualist scene in America, and that it was more respectable to ally with the more sophisticated Boston Brahmins (i.e., the New England Transcendentalists) and academic Orientalists like Max Muller and Paul Deussen. The irony is that many of his own best friends (notably, the distinguished judge Subramanian Iyer) were ardent Theosophists and he had to persuade his followers from joining the Theosophical Society. As Emilsen puts it, Vivekananda's movement had become "like a gecko, almost indistinguishable from the Theosophists."[86]

Through the intellectual currents that led Hindu reformers like Keshub Chunder Sen and Vivekananda away from accepting sacred books on faith alone, there was one reform movement which stood steadfast for trusting nothing but the Vedas. This was the Arya Samaj of Swami Dayananda, who was the first ally of the Theosophical Society in India: when Blavatsky and Olcott landed in India, they came as disciples of Dayananda and even agreed to merge their own society into his as "the Theosophical Society of the Arya Samaj of India". The relationship did not last long, and by 1882 Dayananda was denouncing the two as Buddhists and atheists who knew nothing of philosophy of yoga but were only good at jugglery and magic tricks.[87]

Even though Vivekananda maintained a stiff-upper lip when it came to the Theosophical Society, above evidence clearly shows that he was in the thick of these crosscutting currents that were Hinduizing and

---

86 Emilsen, p. 216. Excerpts from Vivekananda's remarks on the Theosophists can be found in this essay.

87 See Dayananda's lecture in March 1882, 'Humbuggery of the Theosophists' at http://www.Blavatskyarchives.com. It is curious that Indian critics, including Dayananda, Ramakrishna, Vivekananda, and later even Gandhi, should have made such a fuss about Blavatsky's pathetic little tricks. India is replete with any number of magic-working holy men who could have taught Blavatsky a lesson or two!

spiritualizing Western esoteric cults, while Theosophizing and scientizing Hinduism. This thesis has found affirmation in a recent book titled *The Yoga Sūtras of Patanjali: A Biography*, written by David Gordon White, an authority on tantra and alchemy:

> Vivekananda's *Raja Yoga* is a palimpsest of the many non-Indian influences …. Although he refused membership in Theosophical Society, there can be no doubt that Vivekananda was influenced by its doctrines, as well perhaps by its position on yoga. …*In many respects, the Theosophists' and Vivekananda's projects were like mirror images of each other. For whereas Madame Blavatsky had earlier grafted Indian terminology and concepts onto Western spiritualism and occultism, Vivekananda grafted terminology and concepts from Western spiritualism and scientism on to Indian spirituality and neo-Vedanta philosophy.* The Theosophical writings turned out to be far more successful in India than in the West, while Vivekananda's lectures and writings have had their most lasting impact in the United States and Europe.[88] [emphasis added]

To sum up this section, secularization of Vedantic spiritual monism – that is, the attempt to adapt the holistic or spiritual-monistic worldview to the empiricist philosophy of mechanistic science – was a dominant trend among the Hindu reformers in the 19th century India. In this, the cultic milieu of America and Britain played a key role by bringing critics of orthodox Trinitarian Christianity, from Unitarians to Theosophists, to the shores of India where they sought a more rational theology. But Indians were by no means passive recipients of their ideas. They actively participated both in appropriating Western ideas and in lending a Hindu hue to them.

9. Vivekananda in America

The cultic milieu that Vivekananda found himself in during his stay in the US was not entirely alien or novel to him. The above two sections have provided enough evidence to show that the Swami was already familiar with many of the spiritualist currents in the West.

My own reading is that Vivekananda found these new religious movements quite congenial to his own evolving worldview. Many in the new religious movements were disenchanted Christians – and this emboldened Vivekananda to loudly and publicly pronounce Chris-

---

88   David Gordon White, 2014, pp. 128-129.

tianity as irrational and superstitious. At the same time, he saw sufficient shared ground between the Western spiritualist movements and the spiritual monism of Vedanta and he wanted Hinduism to take the mantle of the original source of *all* varieties of spiritualism, Western and Eastern. He repeatedly states in *Raja Yoga* that while the assorted faith-healers, spiritualists, Christian Scientists in the West have "only stumbled upon the discovery of a spiritual force linking cosmos and the man", it is only the yoga tradition that offers a reasoned and well-tested understanding of this force. He asserts that such groups are actually doing yoga, even though they don't know it: "wherever any sect of body of people is trying to search out anything occult and mystical, or hidden, what they are doing is really yoga" (*CW*, 1, p. 159).

Raja Yoga, the founding text of modern yoga, was thus born out of Vivekananda's self-conscious positioning of yoga as the mother-tradition of *all* spirit-centered, esoteric religious movements. But writing at the close of the 19th century which was deeply infused with Newtonian faith in empirical science, and a Darwinian sense of evolutionary progress, Vivekananda faced a problem: How to present the millennia-old *Yoga Sūtras* in a manner that would make them relevant to his post-Enlightenment audiences in the United States? His strategy was simple: he would find analogues in modern physics, physiology and evolutionary biology to propound the metaphysics of yoga.

In appropriating science as an ally of yoga philosophy he was actually following the pattern of "secularization of esotericism" described by Wouter Hanegraaff in his important work, *New Age Religions in Western Culture: Esotericism in the Mirror of Secular Thought*. According to Hanegraaff, esoteric traditions in the West underwent a radical makeover as they tried to come to terms with a disenchanted world of mechanical philosophy and mathematically precise, experimentally verifiable cause-and-effect relationships that rose in prominence after the Scientific Revolution. One stream of Western esotericism (what Hanegraaff calls "Occultism") accepts the Newtonian worldview of mechanical causality and tries to adapt to it, while the other stream (what Hanegraaff calls "Romanticism") rejects any compromise and tries to re-enchant the world.

Theosophy, and some other spiritualist movements like Mesmerism, Swedenborgianism, Christian Science, clearly belong to the occultist stream which sought to adapt to Newtonian and Darwinian breakthroughs. But how did these movements manage to keep their spirit-drenched understanding of cosmos intact while claiming to be in harmony with the essentially mechanistic worldview that emerged after Newton and Darwin? How did they manage to claim "harmony" between two ways of looking at the world which are diametrically opposed to each other?

The answer to this question holds the key to understanding not just Western esotericism and its contemporary incarnation, the New Age, but also the emergence of Vivekananda's neo-yoga and neo-Hinduism. Hanegraaff claims that the secularization of esotericism took the form of "syncretism between *magia* [magic] and science, between correspondences and mechanical causality".[89] What happened was this: *the esoteric/spiritualist movements simply overlaid a framework of mechanical cause-and-effect on the older set of correspondence relations.* In other words, the magical cause-and-effect based upon "sympathies", "correspondences" and "resemblances" were not rejected, but only restated in terms of mechanical causality of "energy", "vibrations" and (today) quantum physics. *This syncretism between magical thinking and instrumental rationality of science was an attempt to appropriate the vocabulary of science while rejecting its materialistic worldview.*

As I have shown in the previous section, this kind of appropriation of science for the defense of spirit-centered metaphysics was already beginning to show up in the circles that Vivekananda was active in before he came to the US. How it influenced his interpretation of *Yoga Sūtras* is what we will look at in the rest of this essay.

10. Vivekananda's scientized *yoga*

Now that I have all the ingredients I need, I will proceed with a close reading of how Vivekananda "actively positions" the *Yoga Sūtra* within the discourse of physics of his time. His translation of Patanjali's text,

---

89   Hanegraaff, 1998, p. 423.

accompanied by his own commentary, appears in the first volume of his *Complete Works*.[90] The text is based upon the lectures he gave in New York, which were later written down and published as a book which became an instant best-seller in the US and Europe.

Patanjali's *Yoga Sūtra* (henceforth *YS*) is a compilation of 195 *sūtra*s, or short aphorisms, ascribed to Patanjali (2nd century BCE). Even though it has become fashionable to use Patanjali's name and *murtis* in trendy yoga studios and ashrams, Patanjali has nothing whatsoever to do with physical *āsana*s, which belong to the *hatha-yoga* tradition. *What Patanjali is interested in is this: how to induce a state of samadhi, or altered consciousness, through which the soul comes to realize that it is actually distinct from the body.* This state of consciousness is to be achieved through quietening the mind through eight-fold practice that involves clean and ethical living, breath control, mental concentration and contemplation. The aim of "Raja Yoga" – as Patanjali's tradition is sometimes called and is the name adopted by Vivekananda – is spiritual freedom, not physical fitness.[91]

Vivekananda opens his *Raja Yoga* with salvos against blind faith and superstitions which he associates *entirely* with the idea of a "god in the clouds", taking a swipe at Abrahamic faiths, especially Christianity. In contrast, he presents Patanjali's *YS* as an enlightened text that surpasses Christianity because it does not invoke a God that is over and above nature, *and* surpasses "materialistic" or "surface" science because it does not deny the existence of miracles or extraordinary phenomena (*CW*1, pp. 121-123). Here Vivekananda turns modern science's hard-won victory over magic and mystery on its head: skepticism toward magical practices is deemed a "failure" of science.[92]

Patanjali succeeds where Christianity and modern science fail, according to the Swami, because Patanjali had perfected a method of accessing the "subtle" levels of nature. "There is no supernatural, says

---

90 All quotations, with their page numbers, that are cited in the body of this chapter are from vol. 1.

91 See Klaus Klostermaier, 1998.

92 Here Vivekananda was in "good" company: similar "failures" of science to explain the occult were offered by Annie Besant and Henry Olcott for their turning to Theosophy.

the yogi, but there are in nature gross manifestations and subtle manifestations" and while the "gross can be easily seen by the senses" only the "the practice of Raja Yoga will lead to the acquisition of more subtle perceptions" (p. 122). *Yogic meditation is simply this science of the subtle:* "the rishis or sages declare they experienced certain truths, and these they preach" (p. 126). While in the "religions of the book", only the original founders/teachers actually experienced God, yoga makes it possible for *everyone* to experience the reality of God. All they have to do is to follow the "scientifically worked out method" of yoga (p. 128).

All this seems vaguely similar to natural theology of Anglican churches through the 17th-18th centuries which sought empirical evidence from nature, rather than from faith, to infer the existence of God.[93] Vivekananda, too, seems to be engaged in a similar endeavor of finding an experiential (albeit non-sensory) basis for affirming the Vedantic conception of divine intelligence. Clearly, Vivekananda shares the modernist impulse of grounding religious beliefs and practice not in faith, or in the literal word of scriptures, but in some kind of experience which could be justified with evidence and reason.

But whereas natural theology in the Christian tradition affirmed a Designer God using experimental evidence from nature, Vivekananda goes in the opposite direction: *he infers facts about nature from the yogic "seeing" of the divine soul within oneself.* He claims that the "certain truths" experienced by yogis are not limited to the soul, but encompass within them external truths about the material world as well, because the "external world is only the gross form of the internal or subtle.... The external world is the effect, the internal the cause" (p. 132). The spirit, in other words, is the primary, or the independent, creative force, while matter is an epiphenomenon of the spirit. From this, Vivekananda infers that *if you can know and control the spiritual force within you, you can know and control the material world:*

> The man who has learned to manipulate the inner forces will get the whole of nature under his control. The yogi [seeks nothing less] than to master the whole universe, to control whole of nature... [The yogi seeks to get to a point] where "nature's laws" have no influence on him [as] he will be beyond them all. *He will be the master of the whole nature, internal and external.* (p. 133)

---

93 John Hedley Brooke (1991) is the most authoritative guide to natural theology.

Suppose a man understood the *prāṇa* perfectly and could control it, what powers of earth would not be his? *He would be able to move the sun and the stars out of their place*, to control everything in the universe, from the atoms to the biggest suns, because he would control the *prāṇa*. (p. 148)

When the yogi becomes perfect, there will be nothing in nature not under his control. *If he orders the gods or the souls of the departed, they will come at his bidding*. All the forces of nature will obey him as slaves ... The yogi ...gains perfection. He becomes almost almighty. (p. 151)

Here, Vivekananda is defending the extraordinary powers (italicized in the quotations above) which clearly defy all known laws of nature that Patanjali promises in *YS*. He not only defends, but celebrates these paranormal powers: "Absolute control of nature, and nothing short of it, must be the goal. We must be the masters and not the slaves of nature" (p. 140).[94] He goes on to celebrate the "Indian race" for the special gift for acquiring inner knowledge that allows control of the outer nature (p. 133).

Vivekananda is clearly and unambiously defending magic.[95] But he has evidently internalized the Theosophist slogan cited above (section 7) that "Magic is only a science" of the "subtle" forces that the "materialistic" Western science is unable to get to. In order to pass Patanjali's 2000 years old Yoga Sutra as "science," Vivekananda ends up distorting both Patanjali *and* science. What is interesting is that the moves he makes in this double-distortion follow the script laid out by the Blavatsky and her followers in the Theosophical Society before him. Let us look at how he proceeds to scientize Patanjali.

Magical powers are certainly of great interest for Patanjali. He devotes the entire third chapter of *YS* (about one-sixth of the text) to the extraordinary powers one gains by single-minded concentration. Some

---

94 Indian ecofeminists, led by Vandana Shiva's much-celebrated 1988 book, *Staying Alive*, like to present Hinduism (especially *Sāṁkhya*) as eco-friendly and women-friendly. Vivekananda's interpretation of *Sāṁkhya-yoga* as absolute domination of nature ought to give them some food for thought.

95 Magic, to put is simply, is the belief that "there are supernatural and spiritual forces that can be controlled through rituals and incantations." These rituals don't necessarily try to draw down supernatural powers of gods, angels or demons. Rather, the so-called "natural magic" tries to control the "occult" or "subtle" forces of nature that supposedly lie beyond the scope of "materialistic" science. See Burton and Grandy, 2004, p. 36.

of these powers (culled from Vivekananda's own translation of Patanjali) are: acquiring the knowledge of past lives, becoming invisible, predicting the time of one's own death, becoming as strong as an elephant, seeing remote things, acquiring knowledge of the Sun, the Moon and the stars, the ability to see spirits of the dead, the ability to "enter a dead body and make it get up and move", the ability to become as "light as cotton-wool" that can fly through the skies, the ability to become "as minute as a particle and as huge as a mountain", the ability to makes blazes of light come out of one's body... and so on (pp. 270-288). In his translation and commentary, Vivekananda defends all these powers as a simple matter of "doing *saṁyama*", which amount to "directing the mind to a particular object and fixing it there and keeping it there for a long time" (p. 271). So, for example, when a yogi does "*saṁyama* on the form of the body... the yogi's body becomes unseen... or he can apparently vanish" (p. 277); or "by making *saṁyama* on the relationship between *akasha* (space) and the body and by becoming light as cotton wool through meditation on them, the yogi goes through the skies" (pp. 282-283), etc.[96]

That *Patanjali* ascribes magical powers to yoga is not surprising, considering he was writing more than 2000 years ago. The question is how could *Vivekananda* defend occult powers at the cusp of the 19th and 20th centuries? How could he hope to get a serious enough hearing, especially after he very grandly declared Hinduism to be a religion of science? Why wasn't he afraid of being laughed at? Why are his writings on yoga *still* taken seriously in the New Age circles in the West, and in the national mainstream in India?

This is where scientization comes in. Vivekananda manages to get away with defending thoroughly discredited superstitions because he dresses them up in the vocabulary of science. How is this scientization accomplished? By completely re-writing the *Sāṁkhya* philosophy, in which he first replaces the material substrate, or *prakṛti* with what he calls "*ākāśa*" and the spiritual principle, and *puruṣa* with "*prāṇa*". He

---

96 What is surprising is that Vivekananda celebrates these occult powers while his own guru, Ramakrishna Parmahansa, had rejected them in no uncertain words: "occult powers are as abominable as the filth of a prostitute". Quoted here from Sharma, 2013, p. 6.

then proceeds to draw resemblances or parallels between *ākāśa* and "ether" and between *prāṇa* and "energy". Both "ether" and "energy" are well-defined, experimentally verifiable concepts derived from Newtonian physics, which was the very paradigm of science in the 19th century. Once these resemblances are established – based upon nothing but a poetic, metaphoric "feel" of sameness – they are brought within the field of empirical science of physics, and take on its aura. Once this identity is established, the control of *prāṇa* through *prāṇāyāma* simply becomes "control of cosmic energy", and the occult powers that result from *prāṇāyāma* become simply a matter of "scientifically" manipulating this "energy".

Vivekananda is celebrated in India as someone who *revived* the yogic and Vedantic tradition. But he wasn't bringing the old back to life in its original form, as much as *re-writing* it and transforming it beyond recognition. He completely rewrote the fundamental categories of *Sāṁkhya* philosophy that is the basis of YS. While *ākāśa* is one of the five basic constituents of nature recognized by Indian philosophy, in *Sāṁkhya*-Yoga philosophy, it is merely a minor evolute of *prakṛti* associated with the sense of sound.[97] It is by no means the primal substance out of which everything has evolved, as Vivekananda describes it: "[*ākāśa* is] the omnipresent all-penetrating existence. Everything that has form, everything that exists.. has evolved out of this *akasha*. It is the *akasha* that becomes the air ... that becomes the sun, the earth, the moon ... it is this *akasha* that becomes the human body, the animal body, the plants ..." (p. 147). The constitutive role he assigns to the "subtle" *ākāśa* ("so subtle that it is beyond all ordinary perception", p. 147) is actually assigned to the category of *prakṛti* in *Sāṁkhya*, where it is not considered as necessarily "subtle".[98]

Even more curious is the elevation of *prāṇa* to the status of the "manifesting power of the universe" (p. 147) – the role that *Sāṁkhya*-

---

97 The other four *bhūtas* are: *pṛthvī* (earth), *āp* (water), *tejas* (fire) and *vāyu* (air) (Hiriyanna, 1993). For a basic outline of *Sāṁkhya* philosophy, see Indira Mahalingam (1997).

98 *Prakṛti* in *Sāṁkhya* philosophy is by no means described as "subtle" and all pervasive: it is both finite and limited in space and time (in its manifest form) and subtle and invisible (in its un-manifest form). See Indira Mahalingam, 1997, p. 162.

Yoga philosophy assigns to *purusha*, the pure or non-material con-sciousness.[99] Patanjali, whose philosophy Vivekananda is expounding upon, devotes all of *one* verse to *prāṇa* where he clearly means nothing more than the act of breathing: "Or the stability of mind is gained by exhaling and retaining the breath."[100] This is all. Controlling the breath is one of the many ways Patanjali recommends for stilling the mind by focusing it on a single object, which can be anything, a *mantra*, an image, or it can be one's own breath.[101] Moreover, *Sāṁkhya* philosophy makes no mention of *prāṇa* at all, not even as a minor evolute of *prakṛti*. If there is any Indian tradition that gives breath-control central role in salvation, it is *haṭha yoga* – the same tradition of bodily yoga that Vive-kananda looked down upon![102]

Vivekananda admits that Patanjali "does not lay much stress on *prāṇa* or *prāṇāyāma*" (p. 223). But that does not prevent him from turning *prāṇa* into the spiritual, vital force of the entire universe. For Patanjali *prāṇa* is simply breath – the air we breathe in and breathe out. Vivekananda announces repeatedly and very clearly that *prāṇa* is *not* breath. Rather:

> *Prāṇāyāma* is not, as many think, something about breath; breath indeed has very little to do with it, if anything. (*CW*1, p. 147)

> *Prāṇa* is not exactly breath. It is the name for the energy that is in the universe. Whatever you see in the universe, whatever moves or works, or has life, is a manifestation of this *prāṇa*. The sum total of the energy displayed in the uni-verse is called *prāṇa*. (p. 223)

So, *prāṇa* is not "exactly" breath, even though it not not-breath ei-ther, for it is by controlling his breathing that a yogi can control what-ever *prāṇa* is! When we breathe in and out, we are not just breathing

---

99 The kind of dualism between the body and the body-free soul that *Sāṁkhya* teaches has been totally defeated in science and philosophy. For a lucid treatment of this subject, see Flanagan (2007).

100 See Bryant's translation, 2009. The verse about breathing is in the first chapter, verse 34.

101 Stilling the mind (*citta*), which is part of *prakṛti*, or the material body, so that you can "see" the pure soul, *puruṣa*, freed from all bodily entanglements is the whole point of yogic meditation in *YS*.

102 "It is the primary aim of *haṭha yoga* to prevent the dissipation of the vital breath, or *prāṇa*… in order to awaken the "serpent force" or *kuṇḍālinī* (King, 1999, p. 71).

in air, this ordinary mixture of nitrogen, oxygen, carbon dioxide and other trace gases. Rather, we are breathing in some kind of disembodied "universal energy" which has the following features:

> Just as *akasha* is the infinite, omnipresent material of the universe, so is *prāṇa* the infinite, omnipresent manifesting power of this universe. (p. 147)

> Out of *prāṇa* is evolved everything we call energy, everything we call force. It is *prāṇa* that is manifesting as gravitation, as magnetism. It is the *prāṇa* that is manifesting as the action of the body, as nerve current, as thought-force. (p. 148)

> ....*prāṇa* is the generalized manifestation of force. (p. 149)

So *prāṇa* is just physical energy, but at the same time, it is a special "spiritual" energy that is responsible for life, mind and consciousness. The same energy that is working outside as electricity and magnetism, Vivekananda claims, is changed into *ojha*s, the state of "super-consciousness" or *samādhi*, when the yogi's mind is vibrating at the same frequency as the subtle universal force, the One, the Absolute Spirit.[103] Processes that characterize life, including those of mental life and consciousness, are not emergent properties of biochemical matter, but rather require the work of "cosmic energy" which is quasi-physical and quasi-spiritual.

Vivekananda makes these radical changes in classical yoga philosophy most nonchalantly and without any explanation. He seems to assume that the categories of *prāṇa* and *ākāsa* were already familiar to his Western audiences and therefore brings them center-stage in his commentary on *YS*, where they actually do not belong at all.

He was not wrong in this assumption: both *ākāsa* as "ether" and *prāṇa* as "energy" were innovations of Theosophists who had taken these words from Sanskrit sources and used them as synonyms of ether and energy of physics. In her *Isis Unveiled* published in 1877 (when Vivekananda was only 14-years old), Madame Blavatsky had already claimed that the universe was bathed in akasha, some kind of subtle ether that she claimed was similar to the "magnetic fluid" of Mesmer. In

---

103 Here, Vivekananda smuggles in the vocabulary of *chakra*s and *kuṇḍālinī*. He interprets these imaginary meditative aids in the *haṭha* yogic tradition as anatomically real nerve structures lying along the spinal cord. Nothing remotely resembling these *chakra*s has ever been detected by neuroscience.

fact, it was through this medium that she claimed to get telepathic messages from her Himalayan masters. Likewise with *prāṇa*-"energy" parallelism, which one finds in her second big book, *The Secret Doctrine*, published in 1885 after Blavatsky had already moved her Society to Adyar. This linkage was picked by her Indian followers. The Theosophist Shrinivas Iyengar, in his translation of the *haṭha yoga* text, *Haṭhayoga Pradīpikā*, published by the Theosophical Society in 1893, borrows this expanded notion of *prāṇa* from the *Secret Doctrine* and makes a clear distinction between *prāṇa* and breathing: "Breath does not mean the air taken in and breathed out, but the *prāṇa*, i.e, the magnetic current of breath."[104] It is well known that just before he started his series of lectures on *YS* Vivekananda had requested his publisher to procure for him a copy of the aforementioned *Haṭhayoga Pradīpikā*, along with copies of *Kūrma Purāṇa* and *Sāṃkhya Kārikā*. It is quite likely, as White suggests, that "if Vivekananda did not take his lead directly from Madame Blavatsky, he may have done so indirectly through his reading of the society's translation of the *Pradīpikā*."[105] Even more importantly, it was the Theosophical Society that put the *YS* on the world map: it is the Theosophists who were the first to publish English translations of Patanjali's great work on yoga, first by Tookarm Tatya in 1885, and M.N. Dvivedi in 1890. In so many ways, then, Vivekananda was walking the talk of the Theosophists – even though he continued to decry them in public.

Coming back to the question at hand, what does this fascination with "subtle fluids" that Vivekananda shared with Theosophists, mesmerists and other spiritual movements, have to do with scientization of yoga? And furthermore, what role does resemblance thinking play in this scientization?

The answer is simple: restating the philosophy of yoga in terms of "subtle invisible fluids" allowed Vivekananda to unify these beliefs with modern science. Although the idea of fluids so "subtle" that they escape all detection circulating in the universe may seem strange to us, this

---

104 Quoted here from White, 2014, pp. 129-30.
105 Quoted here from White, 2014, p. 129. White uses "Little Lamps", as the title of
   Pradīpikā.

corresponded to the concept of ether that was accepted as the cutting edge science in the 19th century: ether (or aether, as it was sometimes spelled) was supposed to be the invisible medium that filled the space through which all waves were transmitted. Thus all wave and wave-like entities – heat, light, magnetism and the newly discovered electromagnetic waves – were thought to be transmitted through some kind of an ether which was invisible, odorless and did not interfere with the physical entity. All attempts to find this invisible ether failed, and finally, Einstein's theory of special relativity eliminated the need to postulate ether. The idea of ether is now only of historical interest, and plays no role in physics.[106]

But this all-pervasive invisible ether was of great value to spiritualists of all shades, for it bore a strong resemblance with what they thought of as disembodied spirit, or the animating force, or the breath of God: they could simply point to the physicist's ether when they wanted to describe the nature of non-material, invisible yet omnipresent spirit. This way, they could appropriate the language of science of their time, without accepting the mechanical philosophy which treated matter as made up of lifeless particles in motion, obeying mathematical laws which could be experimentally checked.

The resemblance between the vital breath that the yogi controls through *prāṇāyāma* and "cosmic energy" of the universe is not a poetic metaphor. As his statements quoted above clearly show, in Vivekananda this equivalence is to be understood in realistic terms: *controlling prāṇa within the body, the yogi in effect, controls the cosmic energy that causes the pull of gravity, magnet force and electric current.* Clearly, this implies a resemblance relation in the strong sense described earlier (see section 5): entities that resemble each other have the same causal agency. Indeed, Vivekananda's strong defense of paranormal powers through yoga makes sense only against this background.

We now have the key to understanding the apparent paradox of Vivekananda defending occult powers of yoga and still claiming to be "scientific". To use Paul Thagard's vocabulary, Vivekananda had made

---

106 For more details on the idea of ether, see the entry on "Ether" in the *Encyclopedia of the Scientific Revolution*, edited by Applebaum (2000).

a "mental leap", an analogy, between the occult *prāṇa* and the physicist idea of energy. But this mental leap landed him not in science but in pseudo science, because he continued to think in terms of resemblances, and not experimentally established correlations, which are the hallmark of science.

This tradition of pseudo science involving *prāṇa* – or what the Chinese call "chi", the Japanese "ki", and the New Age "touch therapists" call "human energy fields", or auras – has only grown in popularity globally. The problem with this is that, despite years of rigorous attempts to detect this so called vital energy and their localized nodes (*chakras*),[107]mainstream science has found *nothing*. If a definite, peer-reviewed case study disproving the ability to detect and manipulate vital energy was needed, it was provided in 1998 by a nine-years old school girl, Emily Rosa. The experiment showed conclusively that experts in "therapeutic touch" who claimed to be able to sense "human energy fields", and "balance" them by moving their hands on a person's body, were unable to detect the presence or absence of Emily's hand under their own when they were behind a screen. Emily had designed this experiment for her 4th grade school fair, and became the youngest person ever to have a scientific publication in any peer-reviewed scientific journal.[108]

The underlying problem with Vivekananda and other spiritualists' equation of spirit with energy, is that energy is a very specific idea in physics which means the capacity for doing work. As such, it is a property of matter, and not a free-floating entity that you can capture out of thin air, as it were, and transmute into consciousness, sentience or awareness at will. *Energy has no consciousness. And consciousness has no unique vibration, no auras, no bio-energetic fields* – that have never been detected by even the most sophisticated instruments. Life and consciousness are properties that emerge out of matter and, as Victor Stenger put it, "the physics and chemistry of living cells is the same as

---

107 Which, for all his dislike of *haṭha yoga*, Vivekananda happily smuggled into *YS* and as he did with *prāṇa*, drew unfounded parallels with the human nervous system revealed by modern medical science.

108 See Rosa, 1998. For a critical look at alternative medicine, see Bausell, 2007.

the physics and chemistry of rocks." No spiritual energy is needed to explain life.[109]

11. Conclusion

The great Hungarian philosopher of science, Imre Lakatos once said that "the problem of the demarcation between science and pseudoscience is not merely a problem of armchair philosophy: it is of vital social and political relevance."

This could not be truer anywhere than it is in India today. All possible lines of demarcation between legitimate science and ideas pretending to be scientific are being erased, with complete disregard of evidence and logic. In the previous chapter we saw the erasure of boundary between mythology and science. In this chapter we have grappled with a far more sophisticated erasure of demarcation between spiritual practice of yoga and scientific empiricism, and between metaphysical concepts (prana, akasha, chakra and the like) and precisely defined and experimentally verifiable and quantifiable concepts like energy, ether and nerve centers.

This second kind of erasure – pioneered in India by Swami Vivekananda – does not recruit gods and goddesses and their supernatural powers. Indeed, the Swami would have looked askance at the attempts of his namesake to invoke Lord Ganesh or Karna from the Mahabharata to make a case for ancient roots of modern medicine. Far from harking back to the age-old myths, Vivekananda grabbed hold of the cutting-edge physics of his time and simply laid it on top of the millennia old guide to spiritual enlightenment, Patanjali's Yoga Sutras. He kept the conceptual framework of the Yoga Sutras – complete with occult powers and all – but simply re-described it in terms borrowed from 19th century physics. How Vivekananda carried out this re-description is a classic example of "resemblance thinking," which has been identified by prominent philosophers of science as a source of pseudoscience and cognitive illusions.

---

109 Stenger, 2007, p. 85.

What Vivekananda started has only grown deeper and wider in India and in the New Age milieu around the world. Fancier concepts from quantum physics and cosmology have replaced ether and energy that Vivekananda had access to at the close of the 19th century. Given the pervasive, and by now almost taken-for-granted equation between an undefined and undefinable spiritual something with physicists' "energy" in some form or the other, it is important that we become cognizant of the pseudo-scientific sophistry that lies behind such enterprises. And it is this sophistry that this chapter has tried to expose.

References

Al Biruni, 1971 [11th century]. *Alberuni's India*. Edited by Aniselie Embree, Translated by Edward Sachau. W.W. Norton and Co.

Allchin, Douglas. 2004. 'Pseudohistory and pseudoscience'. *Science and Education*, 13: 179-195

Alter, Joseph.2004. *Yoga in Modern India*. Princeton, New Jersey: Princeton University Press

Ambedkar, B.R. 2013 [1936]. *Annihilation of Caste: The Annotated Critical Edition*. Edited and annotated by S. Anand. New Delhi: Navayana.

Applebaum, Wilbur. 2000. *The Encyclopedia of the Scientific Revolution: From Copernicus to Newton*. New York, Garland Publishing Co.

Ashworth, William. 2003. 'Christianity and the mechanistic universe' in David Lindberg and Ronald Numbers (eds.) *When Science and Christianity Meet*, Chicago: University of Chicago Press. Pp.61-84

Bagchi, Prabodh Chandra. 2008 [1944]. *India and China: A Thousand Years of Cultural Relations*. New Delhi: Munshiram Manoharlal Publishers.

Batra, Dinanath. 2014. *Bharatiya Shiksha ka Swaroop*. New Delhi: Prabhat Prakashan.

Bausell, R. Barker. 2007. *Snake-oil Science: The Truth about Complementary and Alternative Medicine*. New York: Oxford University Press.

Bharati, Agehananda 1970. 'The Hindu Renaissance and its apologetic patterns'. *The Journal of Asian Studies*, 29 (2), 267-287.

Boghossian, Paul. 1996. 'What the Sokal Hoax ought to teach us'. *Times Literary Supplement*, Dec. 20.

Boyer, Carl. 1944. 'Fundamental steps in the development of numeration.' *Isis*, vol. 35: 153-168.

Brooke, John Hedley. 1991. *Science and Religion: Some Historical Perspectives.* Cambridge University Press.

Brown, Mackenzie C. 2012. *Hindu Perspectives on Evolution: Darwin, Dharma and Design.* New York: Routledge.

—— 2007. 'The western roots of avataric evolution in colonial India.' *Zygon*, Vol. 42(2): 423-447.

Bryant, Edwin 2009. *The Yoga Sutras of Patanjali.* New York:Farrar Straus and Giroux.

Burton, Dan and David Grandy. 2004. *Magic, Mystery and Science: The Occult in Western Civilization.* Bloomington: Indiana University Press.

Burton, David. 2011. *The History of Mathematics: An Introduction.* NY: McGraw Hill.

Butterfield, Herbert. 1965. *The Whig Interpretation of History.* W.W. Norton.

Campbell, Bruce. 1980. *Ancient Wisdom Revived: A History of the Theosophical Movement.* Berkeley: University of California Press.

Campbell, Colin. 1972. 'The cult, the cultic milieu and secularization,' *Sociological Yearbook of Religion in Britain*, 5: 119-136. Reproduced in *The Cultic Milieu: Oppositional Subcultures in the Age of Globalization*, ed. Jeffrey Kaplan and Helene Low, Walnut Creek: Altamira Press.

Chakraborty, Pratik. 2000. 'Science, nationalism and colonial contestations: P.C. Ray and his Hindu Chemistry.' *The Indian Economic and Social History Review*, 37 (2): 185-213.

Chrisomalis, Stephen. 2010. *Numerical Notation: A Comparative History.* Cambridge University Press.

Cohen, Floris, H. 2010. *How Modern Science came into the World: Four Civilizations, One 17th century Breakthrough.* Amsterdam: Amsterdam University Press.

Cohen, Floris, H. 1994. *The Scientific Revolution: A Historiographical Inquiry.* Chicago: University of Chicago Press.

Conner, Clifford. D. 2005. *A People's History of Science: Miners, Midwives and "Low Mechaniks."* New York, Nation Books.

Cremo, Michael. 2003. *Human Devolution: A Vedic Alternative to Darwin's Theory.* Torchlight Publications.

Dasgupta, S. N. 2000[1922]. *History of Indian Philosophy*. Motilal Banarsidass.

Datta, Amartya K. 2002. 'Mathematics in ancient India.' *Resonance*, April issue.

Datta, Bhibhutibhusan and Avadhesh Naryan Singh. 1938. *History of Hindu Mathematics: A Sourcebook*. Bombay: Asia Publishing House.

De Michelis, Elizabeth. 2005. *A History of Modern Yoga: Patanjali and Western Esotericism*. Bloomsbury Academic

Deb, B.M. 2015. *The Peacock in Splendor: Science, Literature and Art in Ancient and Medieval India*. Kolkata: Vishva Bharati.

Doniger, Wendy. 2014. 'Censorship by the Batra Brigade.' *New York Review of Books*, May 8.

Doniger, Wendy and Brian K. Smith. 1991. *The Laws of Manu*. NY: Penguin Classics.

Emilsen, William. 1984. 'Vivekananda and the Theosophists.' *Journal of Indian History*, 62: 199-216.

Engler, Steven. 2003. " Science' vs. 'Religion' in classical Ayurveda.' *Numen*, 50: 416-463.

Fagan, Garrett. 2006. 'Diagnosing pseudoarcheology.' In Garrett Fagan ed. *Archaeological Fantasies: How Pseudoarcheology Misrepresents the Past and Misleads the Public*, Routledge. Pp. 23-47.

Farquhar, J.N. 1998[1915]. *Modern Religious Movements in India*. New Delhi: Munshiram Manoharlal Publishers Pvt. Ltd.

Feuerstein, Georg, Subhash Kak and David Frawley. 1995. *In Search of the Cradle of Civilization: New Light on Ancient India*. Wheaton, Ill: Quest Books.

Filliozat, Pierre-Sylvain. 2004. 'Ancient Sanskrit mathematics: An oral tradition and a written literature. In K. Chemla (ed.) *History of Science, History of Text*. The Netherlands, Springer. Pp 137-157.

Fischer, David Hackett. 1970. *Historians' Fallacies: Toward a Logic of Historical Thought*. New York: Harper Perennial.

Flanagan, Owen. 2007. *The Really Hard Problem: Meaning in a Material World*. Boston: MIT Press.

Flood, Gavin. 2005. *The Blackwell Companion to Hinduism*. Wiley-Blackwell.

Foucault, Michel. 1994 [1970]. *The Order of Things: An Archeology of the Human Sciences*. New York: Vintage Books.

Gilovich, Thomas and Kenneth Savitsky. 1996. 'Like goes with like: The role of representativeness in erroneous and pseudoscientific beliefs.' *The Skeptical Inquirer*, 20 (2): 34-40.

Godwin, Joscelyn. 1994. *The Theosophical Enlightenment*. Albany: State University of New York.

Goodrick-Clarke, Nicholas (2008). *The Western Esoteric Traditions: A Historical Introduction*. New York: Oxford University Press.

Gordin, Michael. 2101. *The Pseudo-science Wars: Immanuel Velikovsky and the Birth of the Modern Fringe*. Chicago: University of Chicago Press.

Gould, Stephen Jay. 1981. *The Mismeasure of Man*. New York: Norton.

Gray, John. 2011. *The Immortalization Commission: Science and the Strange Quest to Cheat Death*. Allen Lane.

Grew, Raymond. 1980. 'The case for comparing histories.' *The American Historical Review*, vol. 85 (4), pp 763-778.

Gupta, Bina. 2012. *Introduction to Indian Philosophy: Perspectives on Reality, Knowledge and Freedom*. NY: Routledge.

Gupta, R. C. 2011. 'India's contribution to Chinese mathematics through the eighth century CE' in B.S. Yadav and M. Mohan (eds.) *Ancient India Leaps into Mathematics*. Springer. Pp. 33-44.

Haack, Susan. (2009). Six Signs of Scientism. Available online at www.uta. edu/.../**Haack**,%20Six%20Signs%20of%20**Scientism**.pdf. Accessed on Sept. 8, 2013. Oct 6, 1995.

Halbfass, Wilhelm. 1988. *India and Europe: An Essay in Understanding*. Albany: State University of New York.

———. 1995. *Philology and Confrontation: Paul Hacker on Traditional and Modern Vedanta*. Albany: State University of New York Press.

Hammer, Olav. 2004. *Claiming Knowledge: Strategies of Epistemology from Theosophy to the New Age*. Leiden: Brill.

Hanegraaff, Wouter. 1998. *New Age Religion and Western Culture: Esotericism in the Mirror of Secular Thought*. Albany: State University of New York.

Harding, Sandra (Ed). 2011. The Postcolonial Science and Technology Studies Reader. Durham: Duke University Press.

Harari, Yuval N. 2011. *Sapiens: A Brief History of Humankind*. London: Harvill Secker.

Hatcher, Brian. 1999. *Eclecticism and Modern Hindu Discourse*. New York: Oxford University Press.

Heath, Thomas. 1921. *A History of Greek Mathematics*. Oxford: Clarendon Press.

Hiriyanna, M. 1993. *Outlines of Indian Philosophy*. Delhi: Motilal Banarsidass.

Hobsbawm, Eric. 1997. *On History*. New York: New Press

Hoernle, A.N.R. 1992 [1888.] 'The Bakshali Manuscript.' D. P. Chattopadhyaya (ed.) *Studies in the History of Science in India. Vol. 2*. New Delhi: Asha Jyoti Publishers.

Holyoak, Keith and Paul Thagard. 1995. *Mental Leaps: Analogy in Creative Thought*. Cambridge, MA: Bradford Book, MIT Press.

Hooykaas, R. 2003. 'The rise of modern science: When and why?' In Marcus Hellyer (ed.) *The Scientific Revolution: The Essential Readings.*, NY: Blackwell. Pp.19-43.

Huff, Toby. 2010. *Intellectual Curiosity and the Scientific Revolution: A Global Perspective*. Cambridge University Press.

Ifrah, Georges. 2000. *The Universal History of Numbers: From Prehistory to the invention of the Computer*. New York: John Wiley and Sons.

Jose, Vinod, K. 2012. 'The emperor uncrowned: The rise of Narendra Modi'. *The Caravan*, March issue.

Joseph Gheverghese Joseph. 2011 *The Crest of the Peacock: Non-European Origins of Mathematics*. Princeton, NJ: Princeton University Press.

Kahn, Charles. 2001. *Pythagoras and the Pythagoreans: A Brief History*. Hackett.

Kahneman, Daniel. 2011. *Thinking, Fast and Slow*. New York: Allen Lane, Penguin Books.

Kak, Subhash. 2005. 'Vedic astronomy and early Indian chronology.' In Edwin Bryant and Laurie Patton (ed.) *The Indo-Aryan Controversy: Evidence and Inference in Indian History*. Routledge. pp309-331

Kakar, Sudhir. 1981. *The Inner World: A Psychoanalytic Study of Childhood and Society in India*. New Delhi: Oxford University Press.

Kanungo, Pralay. 2013. 'What is Hindutva's connection with Vivekananda? 'Frontline, Jan 26- Feb 08.

Kaplan, Robert. 1999. *Nothing That Is: A Natural History of Zero*. New York: Oxford University Press.

Katz, Victor. 2009. *History of Mathematics: An Introduction.* 3rd Edition. Boston: Addison-Wesley.

Keller, Agathe. 2012. 'Overlooking mathematical justifications in the Sanskrit tradition: the nuanced case of G.F.W. Thibaut.' In Karine Chemla (ed.). *History of Mathematical Proof in Ancient Traditions.* Cambridge, UK: Cambridge University Press.

King, Richard. 1999. *Indian Philosophy: An Introduction to Hindu and Buddhist Thought.* Washington D.C.: Georgetown University Press.

———. 1999a. *Orientalism and Religion: Postcolonial Theory, India and the Mystic East.* New York: Routledge.

Klostermaier, Klaus. 1998. *A Concise Encyclopedia of Hinduism.* Oxford: Oneworld.

Koertge, Noretta. *A House Built on Sand: Exposing Postmodernist Myths About Science.* Oxford University Press.

Koestler, Arthur.1990 [1959]. *The Sleepwalkers.* New York: Penguin.

Kopf, David. 1979. The *Brahmo Samaj and the Shaping of the Modern Indian Mind.* New Jersey: Princeton University Press.

Kragh, Helge. 1987. *An Introduction to the Historiography of Science.* Cambridge University Press.

Kuhn, Thomas. 1996[1962]. *The Structure of Scientific Revolutions.* University of Chicago Press. Third edition.

Kutumbiah, P. 1999[1962]. *Ancient Indian Medicine.* New Delhi: Orient Longman.

Lakatos, Imre. 1981 [1974]. 'Science and Pseudoscience,' in Stuart Brown, John Fauvel and Ruth Finnegan (eds.) *Conceptions of Inquiry: A Reader.* Routledge and Open University.

Lam, Lay-Yong and, Ang Tian Se. 2004. *Fleeting Footsteps: Tracing the conception of Arithmetic and Algebra in Ancient China.* Singapore: World Scientific Publishers.

Lindberg, David. 2007. *The Beginnings of Western Science.* Chicago: University of Chicago Press.

Lipner, Julius. 1989. 'The classical Hindu view on abortion and the moral status of the unborn.' In Harold Coward (ed.) *Hindu Ethics: Purity, Abortion and Euthanasia.* Albany: SUNY Press. Pp. 41-70.

Lloyd, G.E.R. 1970. *Early Greek Science: From Thales to Aristotle*. New York: Norton.

Lowenthal, David. 1998. *The Heritage Crusade and the Spoils of History*. Cambridge University Press.

Mahalingam, Indira. 1997. 'Sankhya Yoga' in Brian Carr and Indira Mahalingam, eds. *The Companion Encyclopedia of Asian Philosophies*. Routledge. Pp. 155-171

Mahner, Martin. 2007. 'Demarcating science from non-science.' In Theo Kuipers (ed.) *General Philosophy of Science: Focal Issues*. Amsterdam: Elsevier. Pp.515-575.

Malhotra, Rajiv. 2015. 'Vedic framework and modern science.' *Swarajya*, Nov. 7.

———. 2011. *Being Different: An Indian Challenge to Western Universalism*. Harper Collins India.

Maor, Eli. 2007. *The Pythagorean Theorem: A 4000 years History*. Princeton University Press.

McEvilley, Thomas. 2002. *The Shape of Ancient Thought: Comparative Studies in Greek and Indian Philosophies*. New York, Allworth Press.

McMahan, David. (2010).' Buddhism as the "Religion of Science": From colonial Ceylon to the laboratory at Harvard.' in J. R. Lewis and O. Hammer (eds.) *Handbook of Religion and the Authority of Science*. Leiden: Brill. Pp. 117-140.

Merzbach, Uta and Carl Boyer. 2011. *History of Mathematics*. Third Edition. John Wiley and Sons.

Michaels, Axel. 2004. *Hinduism: Past and Present*. Princeton: Princeton University Press.

Mlodinow, Leonard. 2001. *Euclid's Window: The Story of Geometry from Parallel lines to Hyperspace*. Free Press.

Muir, J. 1990 [1861]. 'Verses illustrating the Charvaka tenets.' In Debiprasad Chattopadhyaya ed. Carvaka/ *Lokayata*. Indian Council of Philosophical Research.

Nanda, Meera. 2010. 'Madame Blavatsky's children: Modern Hindu encounters with Darwinism,' in J. R. Lewis and O. Hammer (eds.) *Handbook of Religion and the Authority of Science*. Leiden: Brill. Pp. 279-344.

———. 2009. *The God Market: How Globalization is making India more Hindu*. New Delhi: Random House.

———. 2004. *Prophets Facing Backward: Postmodern Critiques of Science and Hindu Nationalism*. New Delhi: Permanent Black.

Narasimha Roddam. 2015. 'The 'historic' storm at Mumbai Science Congress.'*Current Science*, Vol. 108, no. 4, 25 Feb.

Needham, Joseph. 1969. *The Great Titration: Science and Society in East and West*. London: George Allen.

Needham, Joseph, Wang Ling. 1959. *Science and Civilization in China:, Mathematics and the Sciences of the Heavens and the Earth, vol3*. Cambridge: Cambridge University Press.

Netz, Reviel. 2002. 'Counter culture: Towards a history of Greek Numeracy. ' *History of Science*, vol xl: 321-352.

Neugebauer, Otto. 1962. *The Exact Sciences in Antiquity*. Harper Row.

Olcott, Henry. 1895. *Theosophy: Religion and Occult Science*. London: George Redway.

Olivelle, Patrick. 2004. *The Law Code of Manu*. New York: Oxford World's Classics.

———. 1996. *Upanishads*. New York: Oxford University Press.

Palter, Robert. 1993. 'Black Athena, Afro-centrism and the History of Science.' *History of Science*, Vol. 31: 227-287.

Pingree, David. 1992.' Hellenophilia versus history of science'. *Isis*, volume 83(4): 554-563.

Plofker, Kim. 2009. *Mathematics in India*. Princeton, NJ: Princeton University Press.

Pollock, Sheldon. 2009. *The Language of the Gods in the World of Men: Sanskrit, Culture, and Power in Premodern India*. Berkeley: University of California Press.

———. 1985. 'The theory of practice and the practice of theory in Indian intellectual history,' *Journal of the American Oriental Society*, vol. 105: 499-519.

Porter, Roy. 1997. *The Greatest Benefit to Mankind: A Medical History of Humanity*. New York: Norton.

Prakash, Gyan. 1994. 'Subaltern studies as postcolonial criticism.' *The American Historical Review*, 99 (5): 1475-1490.

Prothero, Stephen. 2003. *American Jesus: How the Son of God became a National Icon*. Farrar, Strauss and Giroux.

Priyadarsi, P. 2007. *Zero is Not the Only Story: Ancient India's Contributions to Modern Science*. New Delhi: India First Foundation.

——. 1993. 'From spiritualism to Theosophy: "Uplifting" a democratic tradition.' *Religion and American Culture*. 3(2): 197-216.

Radhakrishnan, Sarvepalli. 1994[1927]. *The Hindu View of Life*. New Delhi: Harper Collins.

Rambachan, Anantanand. 1994. *The Limits of Scriptures: Vivekananda's Reinterpretation of the Vedas*. Honolulu: University of Hawaii Press.

Ray, P.C. 1992 [1918]. 'Chemistry in Ancient India.' In Debiprasad Chattopadhyaya (ed.) *Studies in the History of Science in India*, vol 1. New Delhi: Asha Jyoti. Pp.344-364.

Restivo, Sal. 1992. *Mathematics in Society and History: Sociological Inquiries*. Kluwer Academic Publishers.

Restivo, Sal. 1978. 'Parallels and paradoxes in modern physics and Eastern mysticism, Part I: A critical reconnaissance.' *Social Studies of Science*, Vol. 8 (2): 143-181.

Rosa, L. E. Rosa, L. Sarner, S. Barrett. 1998.' A Close Look at Therapeutic Touch.' *Journal of the American Medical Association*, 279(13):1005–1010.

Ross, Sydney. 1962. 'Scientist: The Story of a Word,' *Annals of Science* 18: 65-85.

Russell, Bertrand. 1945. *A History of Western Philosophy*. New York: Simon and Schuster.

Sarda, Har Bilas. 2003[1901]. *Hindu Superiority*. Rupa Publishers

Sarukkai, Sundar. 2014. 'Indian experiences with science: Considerations for history, philosophy and science education.' In Michael R. Matthews, ed., *International Handbook of Research in History, Philosophy and Science Teaching*. Dordrecht: Springer. Pp. 1691-1719.

Schwartz, James. 2008. *In Pursuit of the Gene: From Darwin to DNA*. Boston: Harvard University Press.

Segal, Robert. 2006. 'Myth,' in Robert Segal ed. *The Blackwell Companion to the Study of Religion*. Blackwell Publishing. pp. 337-355.

Seidenberg, A. 1962. 'The ritual origin of geometry.' *Archive for History of Exact Sciences*, Vol. 1, No. 5. pp. 488-527.

Seife, Charles. 2000. *Zero: The Biography of a Dangerous Idea*. New York: Penguin.

Sewell, William. 1967. 'Marc Bloch and the logic of comparative history.' *History and Theory*, 6(2): 208-218.

Sharma, Jyotirmaya. 2013. *Cosmic Love and Human Apathy: Swami Vivekananda's Restatement of Religion*. New Delhi: Harpers Collins.

———. 2007. *Terrifying Vision: M.S. Golwalker, the RSS and India*. New Delhi: Penguin/Viking.

Sharf, Robert H. 1998. "Experience" in Marc Taylor (ed.) *Critical Terms for Religious Studies*. Chicago: University of Chicago Press. Pp.94-116

Sharma, Arvind. 1998. 'Swami Dayananda Sarasvati.' In Robert D. Baird (ed.) Religions in Modern India. New Delhi: Manohar.

Shourie, Arun. Myths about the Swami, Part I, Jan 31, 1993, available at http://www.hindunet.org/hvk/articles/1206/156.html

Shridharan, Krishnalal. 1941. *My India, My America*. New York: Halcyon House.

Smith, Brian K. 1998. *Reflections on Resemblance, Ritual and Religion*, New Delhi: Motilal Banarsidass.

Smith, David. 2004. 'Nietzsche's Hinduism, Nietzsche's India: Another look.' *Journal of Nietzsche Studies*, 28:37-56.

Sokal, Alan 2006. ' Pseudoscience and postmodernism: Antagonists of fellow travelers?' In Garrett G. Fagan (Ed.), *Archaeological Fantasies*. New York: Routledge. Pp. 286-361.

———. 1996. 'Transgressing the boundaries: Towards a transformative hermeneutics of quantum gravity.' *Social Text*, 46-47: 217-252.

Spoerhase, Carlos, 2008. 'Presentism and precursorship in intellectual history. '*Culture, Theory and Critique*, 49 (1): 49-72.

Srinivas, M.D. 2008. 'Proofs in Indian Mathematics.' In Helaine Selin (ed.), *Encyclopedia of History of Science, Technology and Medicine in Non-Western Cultures*. Springer-Verlag. Pp.1831-1836.

Stenger, Victor. 2007. *God, the Failed Hypothesis*. Amherst: Prometheus Press.

Struik, Dirk. 1987 [1948]. *A Concise History of Mathematics*. Fourth Edition. New York: Dover.

Stewart, Ian. 2007. *The Story of Mathematics.* Qurecus.

Swetz, Frank and T.I. Kao. 1977. *Was Pythagoras Chinese?* Pennsylvania State University Press.

Thagard, Paul. 2010 'Evolution, creation and the philosophy of science.' http://cogsci.uwaterloo.ca/Articles/thagard.evolution.routledge.2010.pdf

Thagard, Paul. 1988. *Computational Philosophy of Science*. Cambridge, MA: Bradford Book, MIT Press.

——. 1980. 'Resemblance, correlation and pseudoscience.' In Marsha P. Hanen, Margaret Osler and Robert Weynet (Eds.), *Science, Pseudoscience and Society* (pp.17-25). Calgary: WIlifred Laurier University Press.

Thapar, Romila (ed.) 2015. *Public Intellectuals in India*. New Delhi: Aleph Book Co.

Thapar, Romila. 1991. 'A historical perspective on the story of Rama.' In S. Gopal (ed.) *Anatomy of a Confrontation: Ayodhya and the Rise of Communal Politics in India*. New York: Penguin Books.

Thibaut, George. 1992[1875]. 'On the Śulvasūtras.' In Debiprasad Chattopadhyaya (ed.) *Studies in the History of Science in India*. Volume2. New Delhi: Asha Jyoti Publishers.

Tidrick, Kathryn. 2006. *Gandhi: A Political and Spiritual Life*. London: Verso.

Tweed, Thomas and Stephen Prothero. 1999. *Asian Religions in America: A Documentary History*. New York: Oxford University Press.

Valiathan, M.S. 2013. *An Introduction to Ayurveda*. Universities Press.

——. 2006. *Towards Ayurvedic Biology: A Decadal Vision Document*. Indian Academy of Science, Bangalore.

Vivekananda, Swami. 2006. *Complete Works of Swami Vivekananda*. Advaita Ashram, Mayavati Memorial edition. 11th Printing.

White, David Gordon. 2014. *The Yoga Sutras of Patanjali: A Biography*. Princeton, NJ: Princeton University Press.

Winchester, Simon. 2008. *The Man Who Loved China*. New York: Harper.

Wujastyk, Dominik. 2009. 'Interpreting the image of the human body in premodern India,' *International Journal of Hindu Studies*, 13 (2): 189-228.

——. 1998. *The Roots of Ayurveda*. Penguin Classics.

Yano, Michio. 2006. 'Oral and written transmission of the exact sciences in Sanskrit.' *Journal of Indian Philosophy*, 34: 143-160.

Young, Robert Fox. 2003. 'Receding from Antiquity: Hindu responses to science and Christianity on the margins of the empire, 1800-1850. In Robert Eric Frykenberg (ed.) *Christians and Missionaries in India: Cross Cultural Communication since 1500*. London: RoutledgeCurzon. Pp. 183-222.

Zilsel, Edgar. 2000 [1942]. 'The sociological roots of science.' *Social Studies of Science*, vol. 30, no. 6, pp. 935-949.

Zysk, Kenneth. 1998. *Asceticism and Healing in Ancient India: Medicine in a Buddhist Monastery.* Delhi: Motilal Banarsidass.

——. 1986. 'The Evolution of Anatomical knowledge in Ancient India.' *Journal of the American Oriental Society.* Vol. 106, 4: 687-705.

Index